Sagas

of the

Air Commandos

Wayne G. Martin

Martin

Printed in the United States of America

First Edition
Published by Uncle Jesse's Workshop
Bookie512@Live.com

To inquire about reprinting selections from this book.
Contact the Author through the Publisher.

ISBN 978-1-7349146-1-0

Edited by

Patricia Farrelly Martin

Cover Art by Blueprintbox.com
http://blueprintbox.com/details.php?image_id=27308&mode=search

This work is a fictionalized telling of true stories. Information was obtained from personal conversations, government records and CHICO reports and general information from sources on the WEB.ie:Historynet. I have cited all published works quoted.

Martin

In memory of my mother and father.

With admiration and gratitude.

They sacrificed everything.

And to my wife Tricia, who is everything to me

Table of Contents

PROLOGUE

The Air Commandos are the Special Forces arm of the United States Air Force. They consist of Combat Controllers, Para-rescue jumpers, Spectre C-130 gunships and several special use aircraft and aircrews. One of the Air Commandos' specialties is creating and running counter insurgencies, (COIN), and they are very good at it. They fly unconventional aircraft to support these operations. They are tough farm boys from Virginia and Ph.D. aeronautical engineers from MIT. They are all volunteers that have been vetted and excel at their jobs. Their modern-day headquarters is Hurlburt Field, Florida. They now have a worldwide mission and you will find them in all parts of the world. Some of them are assigned to JSOC, The Joint Special Operations Command. They will be a part of specialized teams put together by JSOC that includes members from the Seals, Delta, Marine RECCE, and Rangers. The major service organizations try to control their operations.

But the Mission still comes down to an aircraft and a
crew of Air Commandos that will do whatever it takes
to save the lives of their brothers or to complete their
assigned Mission. We are the quiet service, there are no
TV shows. Most people do not even know we exist.

As it was in World War II, Korea, and Vietnam,

it is tonight

Anytime, Anyplace

When you are presented with an opportunity to save
someone's life, it is an honor and a privilege to do
whatever it takes. [Martin]

1

of the

Sagas of the Air Commandos

We're Coming to Get You

or

The Tale of a Rescue at Kham Duc

Tick, tick, tick. The clock on the wall was relentlessly marking the passage of time. The old man sat in his wheelchair and stared at the clock, wondering how much longer. He was 94 years old. He was in a wheelchair because of arthritis and pain from living a rough and tumble life. He looked back upon his life daily and wondered how he had become trapped in this broken body. Though his mind was still sharp, his body was deteriorated to the point that he needed help to even go to the bathroom, help which he accepted docilely because he knew he could not function without it. Every day he thought of the great men he had worked with in his life and the great adventures they had had. He had been a career Air Force Pilot, and had flown special operations almost his entire career. The old man had done things and seen things that normal people couldn't even dream about. The clock told him that his only friend would be here soon. He was always punctual. He came every Tuesday and Thursday. He picked him up on holidays and took him to his house by the lake. They used to go on boat rides, but not anymore. The old man was grateful for his friendship.

The man coming to see him was Jesse, like the outlaw. The old man knew his real name, but, the two of them had used aliases for so long it became a habit.

The old man was known as Elder. He did not like the name when it was given to him, but it stuck, as nicknames often did. It became his main alias. He is now referred to as the old man, but only behind his back. He had joined the Army in 1942 and had gone to flight training. He had never been in an airplane. He graduated from flight training as a second lieutenant in the U.S. Army Air Corp. Most of his class were assigned to bombers. He was assigned to transports. He would be flying the C-47 Dakota.

He was sent to Australia and then re-assigned to his flight squadron. He was a co-pilot flying supply missions throughout the Pacific. He qualified quickly as an Aircraft commander and then as an instructor pilot. He walked into his operations hootch one day and his commander ask him to come into his office. The commander told him of this Brit commander named Ord Wingate and his plan to take his commandos into the jungle in Burma and attack the Japanese from the jungle. Elder looked at his commander and asked how they would be re-supplied.

Martin

He was told that he and other volunteers would fly over the hump and airdrop supplies as they were needed. Elder thought about it for a minute and then volunteered because he thought it would be fun. Thus, he joined the first incarnation of the Air Commandos, the first Special Operations Wing. The old man and his crew flew the hump in C-47's and airdropped supplies to Wingate and his boys wherever they were needed. This was some rough flying. You had to be a man back then. There was no fly by wire, it was all fly by cable with no hydraulic assist. You had to muscle this thing through the air and through the mountains of Southeast Asia. Little did the old man know that his last campaign would be in the same theater.

Jesse pulled into the parking lot of the nursing home. He was here today, as he was every Tuesday and Thursday to see the old man, Elder. Jesse had known the old man what seemed like his entire life. He had been just a boy when he met the old man.

He parked as close to the door as possible. The old man was wheelchair bound because of his arthritis and a myriad of other injuries over time. Jesse was feeling the onslaught of the same conditions.

Martin

When he talked to God, he always mentioned he would like to leave this world on his feet, not as an invalid. He entered the nursing home through the front door and approached the nurses station. "How is the old man today?" he asked. The nurse looked up, smiled, and told him he was about the same. Jesse had brought the latest edition of the Air Commando Journal. He would read it to the old man and they would laugh at how different it was today. The nurse was named Tricia and she had been a nurse for thirty-two years. She knew that this was the last stop for these old warriors. Some of them were there because they were destitute and still, every day, they blamed the war for not making anything of themselves. But then there were the ones like the old man. A decorated warrior, veteran of three wars and countless skirmishes. He was there because he had no one else to take care of him.

The Veterans Administration had assigned him to the home when it became apparent that he could not take care of himself. His young friend, in his late 60's, made sure he was put in a home that was within visiting range. He came every week. On holidays Jesse came with his son and they checked the old man out and took him home with them.

They would bring him back with some new clothes and some cookies. Jesse walked in the door today; some days he had to rely on a cane. Such was the encroachment of the arthritis. He always smiled and greeted Tricia warmly. He knew she took special care of the old man. Tricia was always amazed at the difference in the old man and Jesse when they got together. Jesse seemed to straighten up as he entered the room and the old man perked right up. He smiled at Tricia as usual and told her he had a new TV for the old man's room in his car. He asked if she would have one of the guys who worked there retrieve it for him. She happily agreed and Jesse went into the reading room to see the old man.

"How are you doing, Colonel?" was always the greeting. "Couldn't be better," was always the response. They had made the old man a bird Colonel just before his retirement. He had always stayed away from command assignments. He was a pilot. His job, as he saw it, was to fly airplanes, and not just airplanes, but special operations aircraft. He flew into harm's way. He was the point of the spear, and he loved it. Normally he would have been forced out after twenty years, but the old man had friends in high places. General Curtis Lemay loved him.

The old man was a 1st Lt. In the Army Air Corps when Jesse was born. He was an old man of forty-five when the twenty-year-old Jesse first became an Air Commando. But now, the two of them seemed to be from the same age group. They had seen and lived through some of the same things; things that would put lesser men into therapy for the rest of their lives. The old man and Jesse looked back on those things as great accomplishments, much like a pro ball player would look back on winning a championship. Their relationship developed over a period of time. In special operations you flew a hard crew. That means you flew with the same guys every day. A C-123 crew consisted of: a command pilot, Elder in this case; an engineer, the Cincinnati Kid; a loadmaster, Jesse; and a co-pilot. Elder was an instructor pilot. Co-pilots only stayed until they could be Aircraft Commander qualified. They then got their own crew. The three crew members lived and worked together as a team. Over a period of time you learned that you could put your life in their hands and they could put their lives in yours. Every day was life and death. You became an adrenaline junkie really fast. Now, the colonel, at 94 and Jesse, at 69, were lifelong friends.

Martin

There was a standing order at the nurses' station to call Jesse if there was any change in the old man's condition. Jesse was committed to not letting the old man die alone. When you fly into harm's way as a team, and you think you are going to die, you want your team around you. The old man would not be afraid, but, when you are about to do something you have never done before, it is good to have the support of someone you trust. The old man told Jesse about operations in Korea. He would start talking and then his eyes would get that faraway look. Jesse and the old man would talk of missions in the past and always, how the major Air Forces needed to get out of their way so they could win the war for them. People that overheard them thought it just bravado, but in so many ways, it was true. Jesse was twelve-years-old when the Vietnam war started. The old man had been flying special operations for twenty years. He was a Lt. Col. In Vietnam, they would not promote him because he would not accept a command position. They wouldn't get rid of him because he was one of their best pilots. Being one of the few WWII pilots, he did not have a college education, but all of the squadron commanders wanted him flying for them. The old man loved Vietnam.

It was like the old days, making up rules and procedures as you went along. Elder was in his element. He seemed to know that this was his last Hurrah. If he took a stateside assignment he would be forced to retire. The younger officers of the Air Commandos understood this and did everything they could to keep Elder right there. Jesse arrived in 1971 fresh out of a year-long selection process. He wasn't called that then. He got that nickname after pulling his pistol on an idiot who had tried to hit Elder. Elder wasn't looking at the time and Jesse did not consider that a fair fight. Needless to say, it caused quite a ruckus. Jesse and Elder were friends for life after that.

They were flying the line out of Phan Rang AB, 30 miles south of Cam Ron Bay, through the pass. Daily re-supply missions could take you the length of Vietnam or into Laos, Cambodia, Thailand, or even North Vietnam. It was different every day. Whenever a combat essential situation came up, the aircraft would be diverted and would fly airdrop or insertions or extractions to save American lives. Needless to say, until the end of the war the Air Commandos did everything they were asked to do and more. As Jesse and the old man settled in for a visit, a couple of maintenance guys came in and set up his new TV.

Martin

The old man loved it. As usual, as things settled
down, the old man would start remembering things and
missions. Jesse loved to hear about Air Commando
missions. The old man looked at Jesse and asked him, "Did I
ever tell you about the rescue at Kham Duc?" Indeed, Elder
had told him about Kham Duc many times, but he loved to
hear it almost as much as the old man liked to tell it. As the
old man started talking, Jesse could see his mind going back
to a different time and place. He looked out the window
and his eyes got that far away look. "We were flying the
line out of Phan Rang, just as you and I used to do.
Remember when you were there, we had a detachment of
the 311th ACS stationed at Da Nang called the Rats. Every
day they would get rumors of a big dust up coming on the
Laotian border. There was a good-sized camp there named
Kham Duc. This was 1968 and it would be the toughest year
of the war. Kham Duc was used by Special Forces to
monitor traffic on the Ho Chi Minh Trail in Laos about ten
miles away. They had local tribesmen as scouts and security
forces and they were picking up the signs of large groups of
enemy soldiers in the area. Now this is not long after Khe
Sanh. We held Khe Sanh with 6,600 Marines against 20,000
North Vietnamese regulars.

The enemy wanted Khe Sanh to be our Dien Bien Phu. That was the battle that ended the French dominance in Vietnam and they wanted Khe Sanh to signal the end of American Involvement. They didn't get Khe Sanh and now they were eliminating all of our Special Forces Camps on the Laotian border. The NVA wanted Kham Duc. They wanted to connect their trail to Highway 14 on the Vietnamese side of the border. The only thing in their way was Kham Duc. We had Special Forces, i.e. Green Berets and South Vietnamese soldiers, or ARVN with their families, and indigenous tribesmen. "They ran scout patrols over on the trail which was ten to fifteen miles away through the jungle. The scouts would note all traffic on the trail so we could follow them to where they parked at night. Catching them parked made for a target rich environment. We had Sandy's, B-26 bombers, and T-6's to just pound the crap out of them while they were in one place. We would go in with them in C-123's as flare ships. Candlesticks was our call sign for night flare missions." The old man smiled as he recounted that the entire7th Air Force had a lower truck count than the Air Commandos had on their own. "They never got it through their heads that you couldn't hit or see anything at 600 mph over the jungle.

Martin

The reason our kill rate was so high is because we were so low and slow. We could loiter over the target and wait for them to show themselves. The Candlesticks took the worst of it. We were so low and so slow and we had to be in a stable run to drop the flares, so any anti-aircraft gunner would key on us right away. We had some birds shot up pretty bad, but we were running a counter insurgency. We had Vietnamese fighting the Vietcong.

"It worked well and would have succeeded, but then the US sent in 500,000 troops. The Vietnamese were more than happy to have the American soldier fight for him. "The 7th Air Force and their Army counterparts became star factories. How many generals can we make? They did not listen to intel from the field. They were more interested in furthering their own careers than what was happening on the battlefield.

"This was 1968. First was the Tet Offensive, a massive insurgency that was country wide. The North thought that it would be enough to get the Americans out of their country or get them to the bargaining table. It didn't work. The North was shocked that we could respond to them in so many different places.

Martin

We retook everything we lost including the Citadel in Hue city. American Marines take whatever territory they want and hold however long they want. After TET there was Khe Sahn - 20,000 NVA regulars against 6,600 Marines.

"We held Khe Sahn against all odds. You can ask my friend Kenny Webb; he was there. The NVA couldn't take Khe Sahn. They wanted that to be our Dien Bien Phu.

"They were not going to run us out of the country the way they did the French. They retreated from Khe Sahn but they did not go home. There were large enemy forces in Laos prowling the border. We discovered an NVA division and a Viet Cong regiment moving into the area around Kham Duc. "All of a sudden, the patrols they were sending out had to watch out for more than just tigers." The old man stopped talking and was just staring out of the window with that faraway look in his eyes. He was reliving one of the best times of his life.

Jesse broke the spell by offering to make a pot of coffee. He made the coffee and handed a cup to the old man. The old man gave that trademark grin of his and pulled a half pint bottle of bourbon from inside the cushion on the back of his chair. They both smiled as he poured a shot into each of their coffee cups. He had given up drinking completely years ago, but this was one pleasure Jesse enjoyed with the old man. Truth is, he brought him

the whiskey and helped him hide it. It was not allowed but
Jesse felt he deserved a drink if he wanted one. He didn't
abuse the privilege; on the contrary, he sometimes forgot
he had it. The taste and the smell bring back memories of a
grand time. After a few minutes Jesse asked the old man
what was going on during the build up to the rescue. "Well,
I was flying the line out of Phan Rang with the 310th. Our
old squadron. It was just like when you and I flew together,
fly five days on, have one off. We'd go into Ops every
morning to get our itinerary; the loadmaster would load
the plane and off we'd go. Another day in Paradise. "Then
we would be diverted to CE or combat essential missions.
Back then we were on our own. All we got from the 834th
was a problem. We had to figure out how to solve it. The
more headquarters meddled in operations, the worse it got.
You saw some of that when you were there". Jesse did
remember that. "Yeah, I did," said Jesse. "Do you
remember that time the ARVN was pulling out of that little
dirt strip and we found that Airman with a Euclid forklift?

They had given him an M-16 and told him to drive it back to base through the pass. Everyone knew the Viet Cong owned that pass and that kid was scared to death." "Yeah, I do remember that," said the old man. "Remember how quick I called Saigon and told them if they wanted that forklift to send a C-130 after it, because I was taking that boy with me." Jesse looked at the old man and marveled at how he could bring back these details with such clarity. "Yeah that kid was some grateful", Jesse said. Jesse's mind went back in time and relived those times when the old man was cussing the "college boys" as he turned off the radio and proceeded to do exactly what he wanted to do.

The Brass threatened Elder many times and it was plain that he did not care. Completing the mission was all he cared about. The old man was staring out of the window and it was obvious he was in another time and place. "I remember 1968," he said. "The NVA thought they were going to win the war and chase us out. After TET they started taking out all of these special forces camps up on the Laotian border. They couldn't get Khe Sahn so they started concentrating on ones that would allow them to hook up the trail with the roads in Vietnam.

That's why they wanted Kham Duc. It was only 10 miles from the trail in Laos and they would have access to highway 14. People talk about Kham Duc like it was a little special forces camp. It wasn't. It had a 4800-ft airstrip. We could take 130's and 123's in there anytime with no problems. There were over 500 ARVN and about 1,000 of what we called civilian irregulars and their families. There was a small group of Green Berets and some advisors that actually ran the place.

"When Khe Sahn came under siege we were diverted there every day. We air landed supplies at first; then, when the runway got blocked by dead airplanes and helicopters, we would airdrop them. During 1968 it seemed like there was a hot LZ somewhere every day. When a large NVA force was detected around Kham Duc we started to re-enforce the place. C-130's and 123's poured supplies and men into Kham Duc. "This was going on because the powers that be in Saigon had decided to hold Kham Duc. It was a wild time. I got shot at more in the first six months of 1968 than at any other time." The old man paused and stared out of the window. He had a smile on his face that few people understood. Jesse understood it and was smiling along with him. He and the old man had been shot at a few times together.

As the old saying goes, when you are in a position where you are absolutely convinced that you are going to die, and you live through it, your life will never be the same. [unknown]Both Jesse and the old man had been in that position more than once. They were both smiling now because they were both alive. Nothing more, simply alive. Another old saying goes "Happiness comes from within you" and it was true.

"Where was I?" said the old man. "Oh yeah, we started to re-enforce Kham Duc. It wasn't long before aircraft started to get ground fire going into and coming out of Kham Duc. We had Sandy's and Tweet's working the hills around the base every day. Our leaders down in Saigon sent a MIKE Force into the base and decided to send them to an old fort a few miles closer to Laos as a forward operating base. The base itself was on full alert status now." The old man stopped and looked into his empty coffee cup and held it out to Jesse. He said wistfully, "This is a long story." Jesse took the cup with a grin and refilled it with coffee and a fresh shot of bourbon. He handed the cup back to the old man who took a sip and looked like he was in deep thought. "They really weren't worried at the time," he said. "There were a couple of Aussies that had taken the MIKE Force to the old fort at Ngok Tavak.

Martin

I still can't pronounce it right. They went in as a
blocking force. Nobody knew then just how many NVA
were out there. The MIKE Force had some tribal
commando's and a CIDG civilian mortar platoon. It wasn't
long after they set up that the Marines inserted two 105's
and the men to crew them. Daily patrols did not turn up
the enemy but did supply the outpost with deer for meat.
Everything was calm and business as usual until early one
morning. It was still dark when a CIDG group approached
the 50 cal. machine guns that guarded the entrance to the
outpost. They identified themselves as friendly and were
allowed to approach. As they got close, they attacked.
From what I could learn later, they used satchel charges on
the 50's and shot the sentries. It was on then. A couple of
companies of NVA entered the camp through the main
entrance. "They used flame throwers to set fire to buildings
and to a stockpile of mortar rounds. As you can imagine, all
hell broke loose. Keep in mind that this is 1968 with Tet,
Khe Sahn, and innumerable little hot spots all over the
country. We would airdrop supplies here and air land fuel
there. We were flying as many sorties a day as we could.
We would leave Phan Rang in the morning and God knows
where we would be that day. We kind of fudged on crew
rest. We were working sixteen-hour days, Combat Essential
missions all day, every day. It was glorious."

The old man paused and stared out of his window. "So, where was I? Oh yes. The NVA and their locals, the VC , are inside the perimeter and they spread out. They say it was close quarter fighting from the get go. The troops there were able to stop the enemy short of the helicopter pads. It was four or five in the morning when our Spooky's showed up. For our first try at a gunship, they worked great. The Spooky's made run after run on the perimeter to hold the enemy back. They would work until they ran out of fuel or ammo and then go to resupply. After daylight the F-4's showed up. Gun runs, bomb runs, and napalm, glorious napalm. They say the NVA machine guns never stopped, and rockets and mortars were raining down on them the entire time. "Now I know no one has ever heard of Ngok Tavak, but it was an important battle. The whole time this is going on, we are reinforcing Kham Duc. The Aussies at the fort were screaming for more support and Medevac helicopters. About 9 or 9:30 that morning we heard on the radio that two big marine helicopters were inbound with troops and supplies. They got in and let the replacements out, but before they could take on wounded, both choppers were shot up on the pad. Now this is not well known, but the army sent in Dust Off Medevac choppers to evacuate the wounded.

Now I didn't see this, but they say that the enemy stopped firing at the Dust Off's that had the big red crosses on them. They allowed those choppers to come in and pick up wounded and leave. You got to respect them for that. This was controlled by the North Vietnamese Army, not some rag tag group of Vietcong. With the wounded out of the fort, the Aussie commander had some decisions to make. He knew that he could not hold another day and night. Early in the day he started requesting napalm runs all along the route the NVA had taken to get to the camp. This was the greatest decision of his career. "They gathered and destroyed all of the weapons they could not use and in a stroke of genius he led his men out of the camp on the route the enemy had used to get there. They were mortared on the way out and took some casualties. They could not stop. One of the Green Beret medics decided on his own to stay with the wounded and was captured with them. He was a true hero. He was willing to give up his own life to comfort others even when he knew what the outcome was going to be. The column traveled through dense jungle until they thought they were safe. They hacked out a helicopter landing zone and called for pickup. Two Marine helicopters went in to pick them up. Their extraction was complete before dark. They were taken to Kham Duc and then extracted out. Their battle was over.

By the time that Ngok Tavak fell that day, Kham Duc was under heavy mortar attack. It was starting to get hairy flying into Kham Duc. We were now flying in supplies and reinforcements from Chu Lai and Da Nang. Ground fire and antiaircraft fire increased daily. Planes and helicopters were being shot down. It was only the beginning. "The way we were sending in reinforcements and supplies led everyone to believe it was going to be another Khe Sahn. We were going to hold it. By May 11th nobody wanted to go to Kham Duc. It was a hot area. All high ground around Kham Duc was either under attack or controlled by the enemy. That night, C-130's brought in more reinforcements and three Air Commando combat controllers to direct airstrikes against the enemy. We had gunships and flare ships making runs on the perimeter all night. By morning, all of the outposts around Kham Duc had fallen to the enemy. Now the crews of the C-130's, the C123's and the helicopters coming into Kham Duc were praying to their god to please let them get out of this hell hole alive. Planes were being shot up and all across the system planes were loading up to come to Kham Duc. Back at headquarters, General Westmoreland, made the decision to evacuate Kham Duc. Imagine this. I am in the air, on my way to Kham Duc with a load of supplies. We get the call that we are to return to Danang to offload our cargo and go to

Kham Duc empty to pick up people and supplies. Well crap!! On the radio we could hear the chaos that ensued. All the aircrews knew that this was really bad. There was very little time to get the people out of Kham Duc and there were hundreds of them. Yes sir, this little snafu was going to be bad. "The bad part was, the people at headquarters who were causing it were thinking about what they would have for lunch. We were wondering if we were going to live to see another day. The Army sent in Chinook helicopters to start the evacuation. The first one was shot up pretty badly and was on fire on the runway. The crew got out, but the thing is now sitting on the runway so nothing else could land. Kham Duc was under full attack.

"The enemy wanted it. Meanwhile we had C-130's and C-123's circling the base in a pattern waiting to get to land. Some guys on the ground used a front-end loader and a bulldozer to clear the runway. The evacuation was on. Now this whole thing is being controlled by the 834th and I don't think they knew exactly what was going on.

"Around 10 o'clock that morning a C-130 came in loaded and got shot up pretty bad and blew a tire. They unloaded the plane and were rushed by a hoard of Vietnamese civilians trying to escape the north Vietnamese. The plane could not take off. They made all of the passengers get off. It took a couple of hours but they were able to saw off the rubber from the blown tire.

Martin

The combat controllers that were there to control air strikes got on board this plane and were flown out to Cam Ron Bay. We had FAC's in the air so they were not needed anymore. "They were flying 0-1's and 0-2's up and down on each side of the runway, directing air strikes. Without the rubber from the blown tire, the C-130 was able to take off. Now this LZ is just plain hot. We were receiving fire from all directions. One of our C-123's landed and picked up over 100 people on the side of the runway.

"Planes and helicopters were in and out as fast as they could drop off loads, refuel, and get back into the air. The people on the ground were hysterical. A C-130 came in and loaded 200 mostly civilian women and children and took off. Anti-aircraft fire brought it down right after takeoff. It went down and exploded. All were lost. The next plane to come in was a C-130 and he was on final when there was an explosion right in front of the plane. He went around and tried it again. You could now hear pilots on the radio telling other pilots to stay away, it was too hot. That 130 went in anyway and he got all shot up but he got out with 100 souls on board. This was a rough evacuation. A lot of people died; I think that everyone involved knew it could have been handled better. The next plane up was a C-130 and he started taking hits from 50's at about 300 ft.

Martin

He landed with the cockpit windows shot out, hit a Marine helicopter and came to rest blocking the end of the runway. A chopper came in and made a heroic rescue of the crew and they made it out. "Some time around three in the afternoon, the enemy penetrated the perimeter and the airfield at Kham Duc." The old man's voice never wavered as he relived that day of so long ago. His mind was the mind of a combat pilot. It was his body that was letting him down. He finished his coffee and just stared out of the window. After a pause Jesse said, "You and I had some hairy times ourselves." The old man looked at me and grinned. "Yes we did, you and I made a good team. Keeping those times in mind, I want you to imagine this. We had been watching this thing hour by hour. It just kept getting worse. The enemy had overrun most of the base. We had fighters, Sandy's and gunships strafing both sides of the shortened runway to rescue these people. Three more C-130's were able to land and get the last of the people out. One of them re-inserted the Combat Control Team. No one to this day knows why. We did all we could. We were in the process of calling it a day and having fighters and bombers come in and destroy the base as well as the enemy, when we heard the pilot of one of the last C-130's start yelling over the radio that there were three Air Commandos down there.

Someone, and I have never found out who, made the decision to re-insert the Combat Control Team. The Combat Control Team consisted of three men. "They had been ordered to go back in to direct airstrikes and rescue flights for the remaining people. When they got there, they found themselves alone. There was no one to be evacuated and Saigon wanted to blow up the base because the enemy had overrun it. They realized their situation and took up a position next to what was left of the runway. The enemy was everywhere, so they had a decision to make, do we surrender or fight to the death. It was a simple decision for an Air Commando. They gathered all of their ammo and prepared to fight. The NVA had over- run the base, but it was going to cost them dearly to get the last of this airfield.

"We were in a holding pattern while all of this is going on. The next plane in line, if you will, is a C-123 and he decides he is going to go get them. This is the NVA's airfield now. There is an enemy machine gun position pinning our Combat Controllers down. They are getting ready for their big finish, and they look up and here comes this big, fat, old C-123 to get them. Now there was a glimmer of hope; their fellow Air Commandos were coming to get them. He slams the plane down in a combat assault landing amid a hail of gunfire. He reverses the props and gets stopped on the shortened runway.

The Combat Controllers ran out of their position toward the plane. The pilot is looking and cannot see the men. He has to takeoff. As the Combat Controllers watched, the plane took off without them. They went back to their position and once again, prepared to fight.

"The crew of the plane had spotted the men as it was taking off. They got on the radio and relayed the info to all planes in the area. He then had to get to Da Nang. His fuel was running low. The next plane up was a C-123 piloted by Joe Jackson. He immediately started his approach to the airfield.

"You know he was asked years later, what went into the decision to go after those men in enemy held territory. He responded that his crew were Air Commandos, there was no decision to be made." [Jackson] The old man paused and wiped his eyes. He and Jesse had been Air Commandos and they knew exactly how he felt. Jesse asked him, "where were you in this chain of events?" The old man looked up and a slight grin came over his face. "I was next."

There was quiet again as the old man looked back out of the window. "Now, Joe Jackson was a fighter pilot in Korea and it was those skills he now called upon. He knew the airfield belonged to the enemy and could not get any hotter.

Martin

He made his approach high and when he neared the
end of the runway, he pushed the nose over into somewhat
of a dive. "The three men on the ground had been in a
certain death situation when they saw another big, fat,
unarmed cargo plane come out of the sky. There was, for a
moment or two, hope. Joe Jackson and his crew were
holding on for dear life as they dove for the end of the
runway. They knew what was about to happen could only
be described as a controlled crash landing. They were
hanging on. He pulled the nose up and the big plane
slammed into the runway. Joe Jackson and his co-pilot
stood on the brakes as they reversed the props. The plane
slowed and came to a stop just feet from the first
obstruction on the runway, a burning helicopter. Jackson
immediately started to turn the plane around and the
loadmaster had the door open and the ramp level and was
looking for the stranded men. Once again, the men ran
towards the C-123 that was to be their only salvation. This
time the loadmaster and the engineer saw them. They told
the pilot that the men were coming and he started to rev up
the engines. The men ran out of their hole firing at the
enemy and leaped upon the aircraft and the loadmaster
yelled that he had them all and to Go! Go! Go! Joe Jackson
was bringing up the throttles when time seemed to stand
still."

You could hear and feel the tension in the old man's voice. "About a hundred yards in front of the aircraft, two NVA soldiers were in the process of firing a shoulder fired 122-millimeter rocket. Joe knew that if they were Americans and the target was that big it would be a certain hit. But they weren't Americans and they did not have American equipment. The rocket came straight at them, fell, bounced on the runway and then just stopped in front of the aircraft. It did not blow up; it was a dud.

"Joe Jackson released the brakes, steered around the rocket, brought the Jets up to 100% and at full throttle was able to take off. He brought the aircraft up at a steep rate of climb. The crew looked back at the runway as they turned out and saw mortars blowing up right where they had been sitting. The men who had been rescued had been given new life. One of them, when put on the radio to their outfit simply said, 'We were dead, and now we are alive.' [Air Force Air Traffic Controller, Historynet] The crew went into normal after-action routine. Joe Jackson asked the crew for a battle damage assessment. One by one they checked in with no damage. The engineer had to come back to see for himself, that there was not one bullet hole in the aircraft. It truly was a miracle. There was very little chatter as they flew back to Danang. The men had all faced death and survived.

Once you are in a position that you absolutely know you are going to die and you survive, you will never be the same. The crew and the Combat Controllers of that day will never be the same. This day and this flight will always be remembered in Air Commando Lore as the Rescue at Kham Duc. The Air Force bombed Kham Duc into oblivion. It will go down in history as a victory for the enemy. The Air Commandos however, chalked it up as a great success. As an earlier Medal of Honor winner said, 'If a man is down, you don't just leave him there.'[Bernard Fisher] He also was awarded his medal for landing his plane in an enemy controlled airfield and picking up one of his downed brethren. It is the Air Commando way. But that is another story." Jesse and the old man were quiet for a while and then Jesse got up and picked up the coffee cups. He washed them in the sink of the old man's bathroom. As Jesse straightened up, they made small talk and Jesse promised to be there on Thursday. They said their goodbyes and as Jesse was leaving, he turned in the doorway and asked the old man, "What is the first thing you say when you wake up in the morning?" The old man looked up at his friend and smiled as he said. "What a fine day to die." Jesse gave him a little salute from the doorway and said, "Me too."

Joe Jackson and Medal of Honor Citation

Photo by USAF photo

The President of the United States of America, in the name of Congress, takes pleasure in presenting the Medal of Honor to Lieutenant Colonel Joe Madison Jackson, United States Air Force, for conspicuous gallantry and intrepidity in action at the risk of his life above and beyond the call of duty while serving with the 311th Air Commando Squadron, 315th Special Operations Wing, in action at Kham Duc,

Republic of Vietnam, on 12 May 1968. Lieutenant Colonel Jackson distinguished himself as Pilot of a C-123 aircraft. Lieutenant Colonel Jackson volunteered to attempt the rescue of a three-man USAF Combat Control Team from the special forces camp at Kham Duc. Hostile forces had overrun the forward outpost and established gun positions on the airstrip. They were raking the camp with small arms, mortars, light and heavy automatic weapons, and recoilless rifle fire. The camp was engulfed in flames and ammunition dumps were continuously exploding and littering the runway with debris. In addition, eight aircraft had been destroyed by the intense enemy fire and one aircraft remained on the runway reducing its usable length to only 2,200 feet. To further complicate the landing, the weather was deteriorating rapidly, thereby permitting only one air strike prior to his landing. Although fully aware of the extreme danger and likely failure of such an attempt, Lieutenant Colonel Jackson elected to land his aircraft and attempt to rescue. Displaying superb airmanship and extraordinary heroism, he landed his aircraft near the point where the combat control team was reported to be hiding. While on the ground, his aircraft was the target of intense hostile fire. A rocket landed in front of the nose of the aircraft but failed to explode.

Once the combat control team was aboard, Lieutenant Colonel Jackson succeeded in getting airborne despite the hostile fire directed across the runway in front of his aircraft. Lieutenant Colonel Jackson's profound concern for his fellow men, at the risk of his life above and beyond the call of duty are in keeping with the highest traditions of the U.S. Air Force and reflect great credit upon himself, and the Armed Forces of his country.

#2

of the

Sagas of the Air Commandos

Saving Lives and Airplanes

The Story of John Levitow

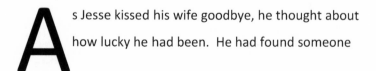

As Jesse kissed his wife goodbye, he thought about how lucky he had been. He had found someone who had put up with him for the twenty years it took him to become a decent human being and had hopefully enjoyed the twenty years since. Not everyone is as fortunate. He was leaving the house today, as he did every Tuesday and Thursday, to go see the old man, Elder. The old man had been his command pilot in Vietnam. They had a lot of shared experiences. The old man had no family left and had been put in a VA nursing home when he couldn't take care of himself. Jesse had made sure it was close enough for visits. The old man was 94 years old. His body was letting him down after a hard and adventuresome life, but his mind was sharp. He felt like he was trapped in a failing body. As Jesse started the 35-mile drive to the nursing home, he thought back to some of the times he and the old man had had. And he thought about the times the old man had had, in a thirty-some year career as an Air Force pilot. The old man was an anomaly in today's Air Force. He had joined the Army Air Force in WWII.

He had a full and wonderful career, most of it in Special Operations. Now he was done and all he had left were stories. The old man had wonderful stories.

Martin

Jesse parked as near the front door of the nursing home as he could. He had arthritis and used a cane, but he refused to get a handicapped plate for his car. He always said there were people who needed it more than he. He walked through the door and admired the new aviary that the home had installed. It was a glass enclosed space with tree branches inside with about ten colorful canaries and parakeets flying around. It was very nice. Several of the wheelchair bound residents were sitting in the lobby just watching the birds. Jesse spoke to Tricia at the nurses' station and asked about the old man. "He's waiting for you," she said with a smile. As always." He walked down the hall to the old man's room. There were no private rooms, so the old man had a roommate sometimes. So far, he had outlived three of them since he had been here. He was waiting for a new one now. He tried not to get to close to them so it wouldn't be so sad when they died. The old man was a pragmatist at the very least. Jesse entered the room and rapped on the door jamb as he did so. The room was always the same. Two single beds with side bars for support, two dressers and a table that held the old man's refrigerator underneath it and his TV on top.

Martin

The old man liked military symmetry. The rocking chair that Jesse had brought him was his only exception.

"Morning, Colonel," was Jesse's usual greeting, "How's it going?" The old man perked right up. "Couldn't be better," was always the response. The old man was sitting in front of the only window and was looking out at the buds on the trees as they became new leaves. Jesse looked out of the window and said, "Wouldn't it be nice if we were reborn like that?" Elder looked up with a grin and said, "How do you know we're not?" Jesse had to grin back and said "I don't," and they both laughed. "How's that boy of yours doing?" Elder asked. Jesse looked at him and responded "doing just fine, working hard and those two boys of his are growing like weeds." "Think we'll get a pilot out of one of 'em?" the old man laughed. "The oldest is ten, so we'll have to wait and see." They both laughed and started talking about current events. Jesse told the old man that he had read on the internet that the Afghan government had scrapped an entire fleet of airplanes that we had given them. The C-27 was a turboprop cargo hauler that really replaced the C-123. It had more power so it could haul more freight and troops. It could land in a short unpaved airstrip and takeoff with a load.

The aircraft had full airdrop capability and was just what was needed in that God-forsaken rock called Afghanistan. The U.S. had given the fleet of aircraft to the Afghans at a cost of 427 million dollars. That did not include pilot training, loadmaster training, or maintenance training. They scrapped the entire fleet for .06 cents per lb. Or 32 thousand dollars. The old man was shocked. The old man had started flying in WWII in a C-47. The Air Force that he retired from was still flying some of those C-47 aircraft. When an individual aircraft got to the point of no return from a maintenance standpoint, it was sent to the boneyard and parts off of it would help keep the rest of them in the air. There was even a company that was completely re-manufacturing C-47's with new wing spars and turboprop engines.

The bottom line was that the Afghan government was completely corrupt. Why we didn't treat them like they were corrupt, I don't know. The old man was livid. "I don't know who is dumber, the Afghans for scrapping perfectly good airplanes, or us for giving them the planes." Jesse could see that the Old Man's blood pressure was rising and thought it might be time to change the subject.

They started to talk about the company that was re-manufacturing the C-47's. The old man said that he would love to fly one of them. "Can you imagine, he said, having hydraulic assist on the controls and all that power?" Jesse told him that if he ever found out one would be close by, that he would pick him and take him to see it. "They probably won't let you fly it, though," he said. The old man had lost his pilot license when he couldn't pass the physical. He looked up at Jesse with a sad look in his eye and said "nobody was going to hire me to fly their damn airplane; they didn't have to take my license."

"Don't worry about that. If we ever want to go flying, we'll just go. We won't tell anyone we don't have a license until we get back," Jesse laughed. They both had a chuckle and the old man said, "if we come back." They both knew it would never happen, but it sure was fun to think about. The old man looked out of the window and started talking about the old airplanes. "You know, the first plane I was assigned to was a C-47. We were the main air transports of the time. As the years went by bigger and better transports came and went. There was a C-46, and a C-124 that they called a gooney bird. It sure was ugly.

"Then there was the C-119 Boxcar, the C-123 Provider, the C-130 Hercules, then the jets. The C-141, the huge C-5 and now the C-17. They all come and go, except for the C-47 and the C-130. Those planes will be flying when the design is 100 years old. Those planes are absolutely perfect for what they do. Somewhere at some time an aircraft designer got it just right." The old man was a wealth of information on Air Force transports. Jesse often asked him questions that got him going one way or another. Jesse looked at the old man and asked him, "what kind of changes did the C-47 go through to stay in service so long?" The old man got a little sparkle in his eye and said, "none really, they just kept finding a mission for the old girl that she was just right for." The old man got that look in his eye that he got when he was thinking of something from long ago. "The only real transformation that I can remember," he said, "was when they converted them to gunships." The Old Man was gearing up for another story. Jesse laid back on the empty bed and got comfortable. "You know, there weren't any gunships before Vietnam. It wasn't that it wasn't thought of, but there never seemed a good combination of gun and platform."

"Everyone knew that cargo planes would be a great platform, but they never got a system that would work. It was 1964 when Capt. John Simons started looking at some research on firing from a plane in a pylon turn.

"In a pylon turn, a spot on the ground stayed in the same position in relation to the aircraft. So, in theory, a plane should be able to train a gun on a target and keep it there while flying. Simon was able to convince enough people so that a test plane was obtained. It was an old C-131 Convair. They had this new gun, the Gau-2A Minigun. They mounted the minigun in the C-131 to fire out of the port, or left side of the aircraft. The tests were conducted at Eglin AFB, Fla. The tests were absolutely successful. A pilot firing the minigun in a pylon turn, could easily destroy his target. This program was going great until a lack of funding shut them down. Basically, everything just stopped."

"Now later that same year, Capt. Ron Terry came back from Vietnam. He had been with a group from the Air Force Systems Command who were reviewing the counter insurgency air operations, and he had taken note of and was impressed by the effectiveness of C-47's and C-123's orbiting target areas as flare ships during night attacks on fortified hamlets.

"He was able to test the C-131 and revive the gunship program. By October of '64, Terry had delivered a C-47D aircraft with 3 miniguns. The Air Commandos made floor mounts for the guns and strapped the miniguns pointing out of the windows on the port side of the aircraft. It worked. Terry and his team landed at Bien Hoa AB in Vietnam on 2 December 1964. He had everything he needed to convert two C-47's into gunships."

The old man paused as if in deep thought. He looked up at Jesse and said, "I'd offer you a drink, but I seem to be all out." Jesse got up off of the bed and said, "that's OK, I will make a pot of coffee." Jesse went over to the coffeepot and took it to the bathroom to fill. While there, he pulled a pint of Jack Daniels out of his pocket. As he returned to the table to make the coffee, he turned to the old man and showed him the bottle of whiskey as he said , "look what I found."

The old man grinned and then admonished him by saying, "you need to let me pay for that." Jesse just looked at him and said, "you can get the next one." The old man scoffed, "that's what you always say." The coffee brewed and cups were poured and laced with the whiskey.

As the two men sipped and enjoyed the coffee the old man looked up and said, "now, where was I? Oh yes, Capt. Terry and his crew arrived in Vietnam. "They refitted two C-47s as gunships and were ready to go by December 15. They turned the two birds over to the 1st Air Commando Squadron for combat testing. They flew under the call sign of Puff. It's first mission assignment was to protect villages and personnel from large enemy attacks. These first gunships were reconfigured flare ships. We'd been using them and the C-123's as night patrols. They would be called when a hamlet or camp came under a large VC attack and they would go over there and light 'em up.

"The VC couldn't be successful without the cover of darkness. So not only did they have the minigun mounts and the ammo containers, they also had big flare racks. That's where the loadmaster came in. He made sure that the aircraft weight and balance was correct so the old girl would continue to fly as she was unloaded over a trouble spot. After supervising the loading of all of the ammo and flares the loadmaster flew the mission as a flare handler or did anything else that needed to be done. I have seen them grab a broom and push piles of spent shell casings out of the door.

"That had to be coordinated with the pilot so the brass didn't fall on the good guys on the ground. Puff's first real successful night came on 23 December 1964. They were called to a Special Forces Camp at a place called..." the old man paused in deep thought, "I think it was Tranh Yend in the delta. They got there 37 minutes after the call. Well old Puff went into a pylon turn and expended 5,000 rounds of ammunition. They broke Charley's attack.

"They were then called to a place called Trung Hung, about 20 miles away. They flew directly there and blunted the attack and forced the enemy to retreat. All of Puff's test missions were successful. On 8 February 1965 a Puff flying over Bong Song fired over 20,000 rounds into the top of a mountain in four hours, killing over 300 enemy soldiers. All in all, this was the best money the Air Force ever spent. As a matter of fact, they called it testing but that gunship was combat ready out of the gate. It went so well that one of the initial Puffs was sent back to the states for training. USAF Headquarters ordered TAC to establish an AC-47 gunship squadron." Jesse marveled at the old man and the sheer amount of information he retained. There was no one else in the world that had been where the old man had been or done what he had done.

Martin

"That was the 4th Air Commando Squadron, by
November of '65; the 4th had five planes and had started
work as a gunship squadron. By the end of the year, 26
airplanes had been converted and training was ongoing at
Forbes AFB, Kansas. In Vietnam, the 4th now had 20 planes.
They scheduled 16 and had four in reserve for attrition. The
Air Force then sent the 4th to Ton Son Nuit AB at Saigon and
assigned them the call sign of Spooky.

"Now this was an incredible plane for its time. A lot
of the medium time pilots did not want to fly the Spooky. It
was a tail dragger, and that is a different bird altogether
from a tricycle gear. But there was always a group of young
guns that lived for the adrenaline. All of a sudden it was the
VC that had something to fear at night." The old man
stared out of the window in deep thought. Jesse had not
been there but he knew the old man had taken his turn
flying the guns. He was the most experienced C-47 pilot
they had. They tried to send him back to the states to train
new crews but the old man would have none of it. He
contacted Gen. Curtis Lemay whom Air Force Headquarters
found out loved the old man. The old man was immediately
re-assigned for in-country combat training.

These were actual combat missions that the old man was an instructor pilot for. He was happy with that. They were quiet for a minute or two and then Jesse realized that the old man was staring into his empty coffee cup. "How about a refill, Colonel?" asked Jesse. "Thought you would never ask." The old man held out his cup with a grin. As he refilled the coffee cups with a splash of Kentucky flavor, Jesse asked the old man, "how long could you stay on station?" The old man looked up and said, "It depends; you could fire each minigun individually and set them to fire either 50 or 100 rounds per second. The guns could put a bullet into every square yard of a football field in less than ten seconds. So, you could stay on station and wreak havoc with the enemy for a long time. They also carried 24 of those big magnesium flares and 24,000 rounds of ammo."

The old man was getting cranked up now and Jesse just settled in to get another history lesson. The old man's knowledge and memory were encyclopedic. "It was in May, of 1966 and they moved the 4th Air Commando Squadron north to Nha Trang AB. It was made part of the new 14th Air Commando Wing. The 3rd Air Commando Squadron was created to become the second AC-47 gunship squadron. They were then re-designated Special Operations Squadrons.

"No one knew why the name change or what it meant; it was just some generals in Saigon making up something to do. The gunships were very effective and requests came in every night for their services. So what we did was look at what was happening in this or that area. If it warranted, we would send one or two planes and crews and all that went with them to be stationed there. That cut down the response time to its bare minimum. By August of 1968 we had airplanes all through the country.

"By the end of the war, those gunships were legendary. There had been a total of 41 gunships. The rest of the C-47's were command and control electronics ships. Of the gunships' we lost 19 altogether, 12 in combat. There were some great crews on the guns. You've heard of John Levitow, haven't you?" asked the old man. Of course, Jesse had heard of John Levitow. John Levitow was the most famous loadmaster in the Air Force. He was one of those guys who had enlisted in the Air Force as something else and was tired of watching the planes fly away, so, he cross trained into the Loadmaster field. And in 1968 he found himself in Vietnam. Not only was he in a war zone, he was flying in gunships. Every boy's dream, right?

"He supervised the loading of the ammo and the flares and then in-flight he would arm a flare and hand it to a gunner by the door. The gunner would then pull a final pin and throw it out the door. Now all of this was tricky. The flare weighed 24 pounds and the airplane was all over the sky at low level."

Jesse had not flown guns by choice. He preferred to go in by way of assault transport and airdrop supplies to someone pinned down or insert or extract special ops teams. So did the old man. John Levitow became the most famous Loadmaster in the United States Air Force on February 24th 1969. He was flying Spooky 71 and had been called to Long Bien. The old man spent a minute or two in thought and then continued with his story. "The Spooky they were on, and I think it was Spooky 71 was on a standard night mission and they were diverted to Long Bien because the VC were attacking the perimeter. The crew was well trained and functioned like Air Commandos. Levitow was not the loadmaster assigned that night. He was taking someone else's place. They flew over to Long Bien and engaged the enemy. The old bird started making pylon turns and engaging the enemy with miniguns. They were dropping the big magnesium parachute flares to light up the enemy for the ground troops to direct their fire.

Martin

"People cannot imagine what it is like inside one of those gunships. You know, but a normal person has no idea. The noise of the engines itself is enough to make a person deaf. You add to that the noise of the wind because you have open gun ports where windows used to be, and an open cargo door. Then, you have a row of miniguns firing. All of this is added to the excitement of someone trying to shoot you down. So, Spooky 71 gets to Long Bien and is in the middle of a hectic night. It was then that the strangest thing in the world happened. Spooky 71 was in the middle of a pylon turn and a mortar round exploded on top of the right wing. I did not even know that mortar rounds flew that high. John Levitow had just armed and handed off a flare to the gunner at the door, when there was a loud explosion, the plane lurched in the air and it felt like something had just ripped the skin off of his back. There was a two-foot hole in the wing and the fuselage was shredded. Everyone in the cargo compartment was wounded badly. Levitow had forty-two wounds on his back. As he came to, he was stunned. The aircraft was only partially under control and was pitching wildly. Everyone was slumped down because of their wounds. He blinked his eyes and tried to focus.

"The noise level was incredible, with the holes in the fuselage and gun ports, people crying out in pain, and pilots screaming on the headset trying to get and maintain control of the aircraft. It was dark, the aircraft was pitching and yawing and John finally focused in on a crewmate who was wounded and bleeding profusely. He crawled over to the man and started to address the wounds and stop the bleeding. And then he saw it. John Levitow with forty-two wounds saw the flare he had just armed and handed off rolling around on the aircraft floor and the final pin was not in it. The flare was smoking. His world stood still. If that flare went off inside the aircraft, the crew members would be burned to death. The flare would melt through the floor of the aircraft, through the control cables and the bottom skin. If that happened, they were all going to die. The aircraft would be totally out of control. The C-47 aircraft had a low wing configuration; in other words, the wing was on the bottom of the fuselage. Because of this all of the control cables were on the bottom under the floor of the cargo compartment. He left his crew mate on the floor of the aircraft and tried to grab the flare. It was big, heavy and seemed to have a life of its own. The aircraft was lurching around in the sky and the flare was rolling and tumbling around.

"Time after time, disregarding his own wounds, John Levitow tried to get his hands on that flare, but to no avail. Levitow had no concept of elapsed time. He watched the flare rolling around and did the only thing he could do. The loadmaster leapt upon the flare and covered it with his body. That stopped the flare from rolling around and he could get his hands on it. He was now holding the instrument of his and his crew's death if it went off. He dragged the flare across the floor towards the open cargo door, leaving a bloody trail from his own wounds. He got to the cargo door and heaved the big flare out into the air. As soon as the flare cleared the aircraft it ignited. The flash briefly lit up the carnage that was the cargo compartment of the aircraft. It was so close that the flash blinded Levitow temporarily. He thought he was dead. Gradually his sight returned and he tried to help others. The pilots got control of the aircraft and were able to bring it safely back to the ground. The pilot, Maj. Kenneth Carpenter, was on his first combat mission as an aircraft commander. He did well."

Jesse was looking out of the window in a pensive mood when he said. "He was in civilian clothes when he went to the White House to receive the Medal.

"They wanted him in uniform, so they found some young sergeant and had him swap clothes with John until after the ceremony. You know what is really funny," said Jesse, without a hint of a smile. "They did not let him re-enlist. He had cross-trained from a career field that you couldn't re up if you were not of a certain rank. But, as a loadmaster, he should have been able to. Can you imagine, letting a guy like that get away?" The old man just shook his head. Jesse asked the old man if he knew what Levitow had done after he got out of the Air Force. The old man still just shook his head. "Well," said Jesse, "he went to work on the behalf of Veterans. He worked for federal and state Veterans agencies. At the time of his death at age 55 from cancer he was the legislative liaison and director of planning for the Conn. Department of Veterans Affairs. The United States Air Force named a new C-17 cargo plane "The Spirit of Sgt. John L. Levitow - a singular distinction."

The old man looked at Jesse and said. "I have flown cargo, guns, and psyops for a long time. There have been many cases where a loadmaster should have been recognized for bravery in action only to have a medal given to the pilot and a lesser accommodation given to the loadmaster." "I know," said Jesse.

"Charlie Shaub should have gotten the Medal of Honor, but they downgraded it to the Air Force Cross." The old man looked up and nodded, "I know about that, it was a damn shame. They got busted up so bad and the only reason that plane made it back and what was left of the crew made it was directly because of Shaub. What do you know about it, Jesse?" "Well, I remember they were going in to resupply An Loc. It was late in the war and we had already turned most of our airplanes over to the Vietnamese. The C-123's should have been making that drop, but as usual, our compatriots couldn't handle the maintenance.

"I think these C-130 boys were coming in from Guam. They flew into the country and loaded up three pallets of ammunition. Charlie Shaub was the lead loadmaster and the second loadmaster was Dave McAleece. It was a combat essential mission so the loadmasters were rigging the load for airdrop as they taxied out. They were rigged for a standard three bundle drop. It was a hot DZ and as they approached An Loc, the aircraft came under intense ground fire. They were past the six-minute warning to drop and had the ramp and the door of the aircraft open, Bullets ripped through the cargo compartment and then the cockpit.

Martin

"Charlie and the other loadmaster, who may have been wounded already, were going to be forced to manually release and drop the load because the ADS switch in the cockpit had been shot out. As they got up and looked at the carnage in the cargo compartment, all hell was breaking loose.

"An engine bleed-air line had been shot loose in the cargo compartment and extremely hot engine bleed air poured into the cargo compartment. It did not just make it hot in the cargo compartment, it was hot enough to burn the skin. Charlie was working feverishly in the cargo compartment, and meanwhile, in the cockpit, the Co-pilot was wounded and the engineer had been killed by groundfire. The pilot worked the controls to keep the aircraft under some form of control. In the cargo compartment it was so hot, that the three bundles of Ammo to be dropped were smoldering. The navigator, to his credit, kept giving airdrop limits over the intercom. When the green light was called Charlie finally got the loads released and out of the back of the airplane. Two of the bundles exploded in the air soon after clearing the aircraft. The third bundle, miraculously, landed on target. I believe it was a soccer field. The insulation in the cargo compartment was on fire and Charlie had to put it out.

"The heat from the bleed air had made the fire
extinguishers so hot that they burned Charlies hands very
badly. He was able to put the fires out and close the ramp.
He tended to the other loadmaster and then went to the
cockpit. There he found the engineer, his best friend, dead,
the co-pilot wounded and the pilot fighting to maintain
control of the aircraft. The pilot, Captain Caldwell, knew he
needed to get to a landing field with medical care. In order
to do that he needed to control the plane. He was able to
close the bleeds on the side of the plane that had been hit
the worst. He shut down #1 and #2 engines and the plane
was still flying so he headed to Ton Son Nhut. As they
approached for the landing, they found that the hydraulics
for gear were shot out. Charlie's hands were burned so
badly he couldn't hand crank the gear down. The second
loadmaster, Dave McAleece, was able to crank them down
in spite of his wounds. As Capt. Caldwell turned final, they
lost the third engine. Caldwell held her steady and landed
the plane at Ton Son Nhut on one engine. Charlie Shaub
was recommended for the Medal of Honor. It was
downgraded to the Air Force Cross. The pilot and Charlie
both got the Air Force Cross. I don't mean to downplay an
Air Force Cross, but Charlie deserved the Medal of Honor. I
think it was a shame he didn't get it."

Martin

The old man looked up and said, "One of the reasons I liked flying cargo was that I always had someone like you to cover my back." Jesse and the old man were quiet for a while. Jesse looked out of the window and saw that the afternoon had flown by again. "Same time next week, Colonel?" asked Jesse. "Where am I going to go?" was the answer as the old man grinned. Jesse made his way to the car just thinking about the lives that they had lived. He grinned all the way home.

John Levitow's Medal of Honor Citation reads as
follows:

For conspicuous gallantry and intrepidity in action at the
risk of his life above and beyond the call of duty. Sgt.
Levitow (then A1C), U.S, Air Force, distinguished himself by
exceptional heroism while assigned as a loadmaster aboard
an AC-47 aircraft flying a night mission in support of Long
Binh Army Post. Sgt. Levitow's aircraft was struck by a
hostile mortar round. The resulting explosion ripped a hole
2 feet in diameter through the wing and fragments made
over 3500 holes in the fuselage. All occupants of the cargo
compartment were wounded and helplessly slammed
against the floor and the fuselage. The explosion tore an
activated flare from the grasp of a crewmember who had
been launching flares to provide illumination for Army
ground troops engaged in combat.

Sgt Levitow, though stunned by the concussion of
the blast and suffering from over 40 fragment wounds in
the back and legs, staggered to his feet and turned to assist
the man nearest to him who had been knocked down and
was bleeding heavily, he was moving his wounded comrade
forward and away from the cargo door when he saw the
smoking flare ahead of him in the aisle.

Realizing the danger involved and completely disregarding his own wounds, Sgt Levitow started toward the burning flare. The aircraft was partially out of control and the flare was rolling wildly from side to side. Sgt. Levitow struggled forward despite the loss of blood from his many wounds and the partial loss of feeling in his right leg. Unable to grasp the rolling flare with his hands he threw himself bodily on the burning flare. Hugging the deadly device to his body he dragged himself back to the rear of the aircraft and hurled the flare through the open cargo door. At that instant the flare separated and ignited in the air, but clear of the aircraft. Sgt. Levitow, by his selfless and heroic actions, saved the aircraft and its entire crew from certain death and destruction. Sgt Levitow's gallantry, his profound concern for his fellow men at the risk of his own life above and beyond the call of duty are in keeping with the highest traditions of the U.S. Air Force and reflect great credit upon himself and the armed forces of his country.

Martin

Photo by, USAF photo

#3

of the

Sagas of the Air Commandos

"When a man is down, you don't just leave him there."
(Fisher)

The Story of Bernard Fisher

and the

Great Rescue in the A Shau Valley

J esse kissed his wife goodbye and went out to the car his son had waiting in the driveway. His son, Ryan, was in his forties now with a nice family. He had been coming with his dad, Jesse, to see the old man for quite a while. He would usually come on holidays so he could help get the old man in the car so he could go home with them. Jesse settled into the car and they made small talk as they went to the nursing home. Ryan would fill Jesse in on family matters and things that were going on with the family. Of course, everyone else in the family knew what was going on, but not Jesse. He would not get on Facebook or any other social media. So, every once in a while, someone would bring him up to date. He listened up to a point; after that point he would just zone out. It wasn't that he did not care. He did care very deeply for his family; he just had a low tolerance for details. In other words, tell him the girl is going to the prom, don't describe the dress to him. Ryan would always ask about the old man's condition. Ryan had known about Elder and then got to know him personally. He would sometimes bring his boys to see him and listen to a story or two. Ryan never let on, but he liked listening to the old man as much as the boys. He remembered one time, he had doubted the veracity of the story and had asked his dad, Jesse, if the story were true.

Jesse just looked at him with a sad expression on his face and told him to get on his computer and look it up. He had done just that, and was amazed that every bit of these stories was true. The things that Elder and his dad had done seemed fantastic, and the old man had 25 more years of it than Jesse. Ryan never doubted one of these stories again. Ryan pulled into the parking lot of the nursing home and parked in one of the handicapped spaces by the front door. Jesse did not use these spaces unless he was having a bad day and had to use his cane. This was one of those days.

Ryan came around to help his dad out of the car, Jesse initially shooed him away, but then accepted the helping hand. "Thank you" Jesse said. Ryan just patted his shoulder and smiled. Jesse looked at him and knew he had a good son. He knew that that was a rare occurrence these days. They made their way into the nursing home lobby. Some of the patients, the old man called them inmates, were in their wheelchairs watching some parakeets in an aviary in the lobby. The little birds were pretty and chirped a happy song. The old Vets would sit and watch them and talk to each other to pass the time. The old man was never one of them. He stayed to himself and Jesse was his only visitor. As far as the old man was concerned, that was enough. Spending time to himself satisfied Elder.

It allowed him to think. Jesse was the same way. Jesse and Ryan checked in with Tricia, the nurse in charge, and asked about Elder's condition. She laughed and said that "he wasn't any grumpier than usual." They all laughed and then headed down the hall to the old man's room. The old man was sitting in his wheelchair and looking out of the window at a really blue springtime sky. "How's it going, Colonel?" came the voice from the doorway. The old man turned sharply and said "never better." Jesse and Ryan entered the room and Elder brightened when he saw Ryan. "Hey there, Young Man, good to see you. How are those boys of yours?" Ryan shook the old man's hand and told him they were growing like weeds and driving their mother crazy. The old man laughed at that and said that one day, "maybe we could make pilots out of them." Everyone laughed. The men sat around and made small talk for a little while and Jesse got up to make a pot of coffee. Ryan loved to talk to Elder. His depth of knowledge of Air Force Special Operations was encyclopedic. Ryan said to the old man, "my boys told me you told them a story about a rescue in the A Shau valley. They couldn't remember all of it and when I asked Dad here, he said to ask you, so here I am. What happened in the A Shau valley in 1966?"

Martin

The old man perked up and said "Well, to answer that, let's go back to 1964 when the American military decided to go from advisors to a big military presence.

"The generals thought that a big military operation would settle this thing once and for all. The Air Commandos were operating a counter-insurgency in Thailand, Laos, Cambodia, and Vietnam, until the big Army and the big Air Force arrived. The Seventh Air Force was running things and they pretty much took over our operations in Vietnam. They were always upset that they couldn't touch us outside of Vietnam. So, when the Generals got their big Army and Air Force, they started looking for how to stop the Viet Cong from attacking and the PAVN, (People's Army of Vietnam) from re-supplying the Viet Cong and infiltrating units into South Vietnam." Jesse interrupted the story with fresh coffee. Elder pulled a pint bottle of Jack Daniels from between the seat cushions in his wheelchair. Jesse and his son Ryan held out their cups and the old man poured a shot into each one. He then poured one into his and tucked the bottle away. Ryan said," Do you ever get caught with that?" The old man grinned and told him that "Once in a while they make a big deal over what they call contraband."

"I keep this bottle here for them to find and take away. I have another one hidden very well. If they take this one, I send your dad the same text I send him if I am running out. I have a phone, and your dad is the only one I call." Jesse looked up from his coffee and said, "Yeah, I get the text, and I stop and pick up a bottle on my way in on my next visit." They all chuckled at that and Elder continued with the story. "Colonel Aderholt had set this thing up. It was a classic counter-insurgency. We were training and using Vietnamese to fight the NVA and the Vietcong. It was going good too. We were holding our own in Thailand, Cambodia and Laos. When the big buildup came, it was a classic case of let's fight the last war we had. The Brass did not listen to Aderholt or anyone. They had their big Army and big Air Force. It had only been ten years or so since the French had been beaten and the UN had divided the country. We were doing exactly what the French had done. Now we were losing fighter planes and having fighter pilots as prisoners of war. We had large Army Units smashing their way through the Jungle and they couldn't figure out why they could not find the Viet Cong." The old man sat circumspect at the window. "The Brass had all of this intel from the CIA and the advisors so they knew where the problem areas were."

The old man was really starting to get into it now. "The North Vietnamese were sending men and supplies into the country on the Ho Chi Minh Trail. It was a loose-knit group of trails coming down the eastern edge of Laos with routes going into South Vietnam. So, the generals decided that we would establish a string of Special Forces camps on these routes to interdict the men and supplies. The most famous ones were Khe Sahn, Cam Duc, and the A Shau valley. The A Shau valley was a 25-mile-long cut in the jungle with high peaks on both sides and it was about one mile wide. It was a main route for the North Vietnamese to bring in supplies and men. The truth is that we never controlled that valley. So, we go in there and plop a Special Forces camp right in the middle of the valley on the southern end. It was manned by U.S. Special Forces, (Green Beret) and CIDG (Civilian Irregular Defense Group). They would send out patrols to identify and interdict supplies coming down the trail. They were about ten miles from the active trail. They would go there, find the enemy and his supplies and then would send in A-26 bombers, A-37's, A1-E's and whatever else and go truck killing. Now I tell ya, that was a true sport. The patrol would bird dog them until they parked for the night. Then, we would send in C-123 flare ships to light 'em up. Once the flares started going off, it was just a matter of expending all ordnance.

"It became obvious to the North that these Special Forces camps on their infiltration routes had to go." Elder got this far away look in his eyes as he took himself back to another time and place. "I tell ya', it was like the fourth of July. You had the big flares lighting things up, you had the enemy tracers coming up at you, and you had A-26's putting a steady stream of fire into them. The AT6's would actually bomb them, so you had explosions on the ground. The first time you see it you wonder how anyone could fly through all that and not be hit. After a while you don't even think about it. You just fly your part of the mission and help your buddies all you can. The funny part is, they did not even need those camps. We were running scout patrols out of Thailand and tracking the same supplies and hitting them every night. But the Seventh Air Force couldn't take credit for that.

"Now, once the North Vietnamese had decided that the A Shau camp had to go, they sent VC patrols to harass the camp almost every day. The Special Forces guys knew what was going on and sent out patrols of Vietnamese to find the enemy. They always came back with no contact and could not find the enemy. Now this was strange because we had A1-E's flying air patrols and they sighted enemy troop buildup and big gun emplacements.

"Still, the patrols would come back with no contact. We all know how that happened. "They were supposed to go out 3-5 clicks and make a sweep on the return. What they really did was get out of sight of the camp and just hang out until it was time to go back. The Vietnamese were not the most ferocious of fighters.

"We kept reporting the buildups and the Green Berets put the camp on alert. Then one day, two defectors wandered into the camp and gave themselves up. They were interrogated by the Green Berets and told them that four battalions of North Vietnamese regulars from 335th division were planning to attack the camp. After that, more patrols were sent out day and night, but no contact was made. Air Commandos were still seeing the buildup of North Vietnamese now that they had Anti- Aircraft guns. On March 8, 1966, the camp was placed on general alert and the camps defensive positions were manned and ready. The North Vietnamese attacked that night. It was brutal. The NVA outnumbered the defenders by a lot. They came at them hard with mortars, machine guns, and wave after wave of infantry. The attack was finally beaten back with the enemy sustaining heavy casualties. Now, normally after being beaten back on a night attack, the enemy would have withdrawn.

"They would not be able to sustain any form of organization because of continuous air attacks. But, and this is important, the weather played into their hands. The clouds were thick and low. Flying into the valley was perilous. Knowing that we would not be able to attack with fighter bombers or much of anything else, they decided to continue the attack." The old man paused in his story to reflect and take a sip of his coffee. Ryan, who had been listening attentively, asked the old man why we did not have a bigger force in the valley if we knew of the buildup. The old man just smiled and said, "We should have. Not only did we know they were coming, but we had a lesson plan. They did this to the French many times. The powers that be, the generals in the big Army and the Big Air Force couldn't see past their own noses. If we wanted to shut down the trail and stop supplies from coming into the country, we should have had three thousand troops in that valley, not one little Special Forces Camp and some Green Beret Advisors." Ryan nodded his head in understanding and Elder continued his story. "During the early hours of March 9, they resumed the attack. They attacked the camp with a continuous rain of mortar rounds damaging communication equipment and taking out some of the defensive positions. We could not get any support aircraft into the valley because of the low cloud ceiling.

Martin

"It was close to 1300 when an AC-47 from the 4th Air Commandos made it to the camp. He was circling the camp and firing on the North Vietnamese. The aircraft had to be very low because of the clouds and being low and slow, got shot up and had to leave. It went down about five miles or so from the camp. They all made it out of the aircraft but were immediately attacked by the North Vietnamese. Of the six crewmen, three were killed and three made it to a pickup point and were rescued later by an Air Force HH-43 rescue chopper. Bernard Fisher and his wingman, Wallace, had arrived flying A1-E aircraft to help defend the fort.

"Fisher barely missed a helicopter that was rescuing the AC-47 crew and the pilot told him how to get into the valley. Fisher and his wingman got into the valley and the command post told them they had to destroy the AC-47 because the guns were still functional and the enemy could get them and turn them on us. Fisher sent Wallace to destroy the gunship and Fisher started hitting the enemy. The people in the camp needed to be re-supplied; the problem was that we could not get any of our birds in there to make the drops. Then an A1-E pilot called up on the radio and said that he had found a hole in the clouds that we could go through and get into the valley.

"Now I want you to picture this. A WW2 fighter airplane doing a spiraling dive through a small hole in the clouds to get into a valley to attack the enemy and, and I emphasize this and, a fat, old, cargo bird like the C-123 is following him down.

Once into the valley, they lined up with the camp, and dropped the supplies. After the drop they had to pull up through the clouds to keep from hitting a mountain. They would break into the clear in the middle of all these other aircraft. It will pucker you up, I'll tell you that. The forward air control guys cleared that end of the valley and C-123's and C7 Caribou made run after run into the valley to re-supply the camp. The A1-E's were about the only attack aircraft that could get in and they made run after run to try to save the camp. Helicopters were called to evacuate the wounded and were having a tough time. Re-enforcements were sitting 30 miles away in Hue. They could not be delivered to the battlefield because of the weather. A lot of the supplies and ammo had landed outside of the main camp and could not be gotten. The defenders of the camp had to dig in for the night." Ryan held up his hand and the old man stopped. "How many enemy soldiers were there?" Elder looked up at the wall and was thinking. He then looked back at Ryan and said "there were over 2,000 North Vietnamese Regulars.

"They had the camp surrounded and had anti-aircraft guns up in the hills. Because of the weather, our guys had to fly really low. The Vietnamese were actually shooting down at them as they flew by. It was just a meat grinder. If the powers that be wanted that valley, they should have had 3,000 marines in there. The defenders of the special forces camp had retreated to the fort. It was triangular in shape and had mortar bunkers at each corner. The North Vietnamese had breached the walls of the fort several times and had been beaten back. Then the defenders had retreated to the northern part of the fort. All night of the 9th of March the NVA shelled the camp. Two C-123's and an AC-47 dropped flares all night. The flares kept the battlefield illuminated so the enemy could not sneak in a large ground attack. Early on the morning of the 10th, Marine A-4's came in and tried to bomb enemy positions. It was about 11 o'clock when the defenders got on the radio and said they could only hold a little longer.

"They could not retrieve the airdrop bundles that were sent to re-supply them. They were going to have to have an emergency extraction to pull the defenders out. Fisher would be awarded the Silver Star for his command duties at the camp at A Shau on March 9th. His wingman, Wallace, would receive a Distinguished Flying Cross.

"On the 10th, Fisher and his wingman, Paco Vasquez were on a mission to provide support to Army troops at Kontum. They were diverted back to the A Shau. There they joined other aircraft who were waiting to get in under the cloud cover.

"One of those planes was piloted by D. "Jump" Myers. Fisher knew Myers from their days of flying fighters for the Air Defense Command. Myers was a hard-bitten fighter pilot; he chain-smoked, drank heavily and flew hard. Fisher on the other hand, did not smoke, did not drink, and was every bit the professional pilot. He loved the Air Force, and the Air Force loved him." Ryan, who had been listening attentively, said. "How did they expect to be able to get those guys out of there in those conditions?" The old man looked at the younger man and smiled, and said. "Son you don't get to pick the conditions, but the people are still there and they need to be rescued. So, no matter what, you have to do everything that you can to get them out. Do you understand that?" Ryan just said "Wow, yes, I understand." "Good," said the old man, continuing. "It was Myers who said there may be a way in off to the west somewhere. Fisher went to take a look and found a hole in the cloud cover. He called his wingman, Paco Vazquez, and Myers and his wingman followed him down into the valley.

Martin

"There was another flight of two A1-E's but Fisher
did not think there was enough room for six planes to
operate in the valley, so he had them stay up top. So, four
A1-E's went into the valley of the shadow of death. They
had to go in trailing formation. Literally, there was not
enough room to go side by side.

"The cloud cover was about six hundred feet higher
than the day before which was good for the fighters but
also good for the enemy. The increased visibility made
shooting down on the aircraft better than before. The
Special Forces camp defenders had been pushed back into
the bunker in the northwest corner of the camp. When
Fisher and his guys got there, the enemy had mounted a
ground attack. The A1-E's attacked the enemy head to head.
They make three strafing runs that killed around 400 North
Vietnamese. On the first pass, one of the planes took a hit
in the canopy and had to break off and go to the nearest
base. Myers was pounded on the second pass. His cockpit
filled with smoke and his plane was on fire. His engine had
quit, but he was too low to use a parachute. He told Fisher
that he would put her down on the airstrip of the camp. He
had no choice. The A1-E's laid down suppressive fire to
allow Myers to land. His cockpit was filled with smoke so
Fisher had to talk him down.

"Now you know that he is landing his plane on an enemy held landing strip," said the old man. "He is cut off from the defenders and his plane might blow up on contact with the ground. Now Myers was going too fast to land with gear on the short runway, so he pulled up his gear and jettisoned his bombs, but when he tried to jettison the centerline fuel tank, it did not release.

"When Myer's plane hit the ground the centerline tank exploded. Myers skidded down the runway trailing flames until it veered off to the side and came to a stop. As soon as the aircraft stopped, it exploded. Fisher, flying cover from above flew over to look at the flaming plane and was shocked to see that Myers had survived. He saw him climb out of the aircraft and run to a ditch where he had some cover. Fisher called in the next flight of A1-E's. One of the pilots, Hague, said later that it was like flying around in Yankee Stadium with the fans in the bleachers firing at you with machine guns. Now four A1-E's attacked the NVA who were moving to get Myers. The attack killed a lot of enemy troops and took some of the pressure off of the fort. Fisher knew that if the enemy soldiers got to Myers, they would kill him."

Elder stretched and Jesse saw that faraway look in his eyes. Ryan was sitting still, just mesmerized, knowing that everything the old man was saying was true.

Martin

"The A1-E's continued to pound the camp to try to keep the defenders and Myers alive. Fisher had called for a rescue helicopter to come and get Myers out. The airborne command post responded a few minutes later that the helicopter was at least 20 minutes out. Fisher knew then that they probably did not know when the chopper would get there.

"The enemy was closing in on Myers and if they got to him, they would kill him. Fisher now thought that he would have to go get Myers. The command post told him the runway was 3500 feet long. He decided that it would be long enough.

"A normal man would have thought that landing a big slow plane on an enemy held runway in full view of the enemy would be suicide. Fisher wrote in his book, Beyond the Call of Duty, that a helicopter could use its door gun to lay down suppressive fire to keep the enemies head down while effecting a rescue, but that he would be defenseless while sitting on the ground. It made no sense to anyone, but Fisher knew he had to try. Myers was one of them, and Fisher would not stand by and let him be killed without trying to rescue him. He would be landing on an enemy held airstrip that was just barely long enough. Anyone looking at the odds would be betting against him.

"There were 15 to 20 anti-aircraft guns lining the valley. There were hundreds of enemy soldiers with automatic weapons. Not only was the length of the runway a concern, but the condition was very bad. If you had to rate it, you would say it was destroyed. It was made of pierced steel planking, or PSP. It wasn't a piece of cake when in good shape; now, it was littered with the debris of battle. It had been hit with shells, so there were not only holes in it, but there were pieces of steel sticking up from the explosions. Pieces of Myers' airplane littered the runway. There was trash everywhere. The defenders of the camp could not help. They were under siege. Fisher was going to have to depend on the other A1-E's for support." The old man got that faraway look in his eyes and he looked over at Ryan. "This may sound unreal or crazy to you, but you have to think about it like this. What if it was you flying that plane and it was one of your boys down there, wouldn't you do whatever you had to do?" Ryan sat silently looking at the old man and just nodded his head. "Now Fisher was going to try to land into the wind to help slow him down, but there was too much smoke. He broke out of the smoke over the runway too far to land. He did get a visual on Myers as he flew by at low level. He powered her up and flew a tight turn and came back at the runway from the other direction.

Martin

"The A1-E's, that he so desperately needed for support ran out of ammo about this time. One after another they called out being Winchester, the code for being out of ammo. They were able to make a couple of passes with ammo and they decided that they would just keep making passes because the enemy did not know that they were out of ammo.

"So that is what they did. Fisher put his plane down on the end of the runway and stood on the brakes. The brakes started to give at 2000 ft and that is when Fisher realized that the runway was not 3500 feet, it was 2500. He overran the end of the runway; he went over a small embankment that helped slow the aircraft and he finally whipped the plane around and skidded into a fuel storage area. His wings barely missed drums of fuel and the tail hit some of them, but he was stopped. His colleagues in the air, the defenders in the fort and Myers could not believe their eyes. It was a miracle. As he taxied back down the runway, he stopped to pick up Myers. It took a little while to stop the aircraft and Myers was running out to catch him. Fisher got the plane stopped and looked back for Myers. Not seeing him, he thought he may have been hit, so he set the parking brake and got out of the cockpit. Myers was at the back of the wing trying to get to the cockpit but the prop wash was blowing him back.

"When Fisher saw him, he cut the throttle risking a stall and pulled Myers into the cockpit head first. Myers looked up and gave a weak smile and said, 'You are one crazy son-of-a-gun'. That is what Fisher said in his book, Beyond the Call of Duty, but, knowing who Myers was, it may have been a little saltier than that." The old man had to chuckle at that, and then he continued. "The aircraft had been under enemy fire since touching down. Bullets continued to hit the aircraft, but its engine still ran. As Myers was pulled aboard Fisher's plane, the rest of the flight made dry passes to keep the enemy's head down. Fisher turned the plane around and realized that there was not enough runway. Now we will never know if Fisher or Myers were praying that day. If they were, we know their prayers were answered; if they weren't, God looked down and took pity on a man who had shown no greater love for his fellow man than to lay down his own life for a friend."

Elder stopped for a moment, he pulled out his handkerchief and dabbed his eyes and blew his nose. Everyone was quiet. "You see," said the old man. "You think different when you just know you are going to die, and thinking like that Fisher pushed the throttles forward all the way and headed to the end of the runway. They say that a cheer went up from the defenders as the plane roared past.

"To his amazement, as the plane went over the overrun, it lifted off the ground. With the engine roaring and bullets hitting the aircraft, Fisher pulled her up and climbed into the 800 ft ceiling to safety. They flew straight to Pleiku; it was the closest base with medical facilities. Medics met them at the tarmac after landing. Miraculously Myers was not hurt that bad. He was singed from the fire, covered with soot from his burning plane, and beaten up a little from the explosions. And, oh yeah, Fisher said he smelled terrible.

"According to Leo Miller, Myers wanted to buy Fisher a year's worth of whiskey, but Fisher did not even drink coffee. Myers did give Fisher a Nikon Camera engraved with A Shau, March 10, 1966. Both Fisher and Myers continued to fly for the USAF. The plane that Fisher flew that day crashed later, but was retrieved and completely restored. The one and only Jump Myers went out to California and flew it back to Wright Patterson Air Force Base, where it is on display. You know," said the old man, "there was something else about that day that was totally unique. I did not find out about this for a long time, but it just points out that Air Commandos are who they are all the time. Back in WWII there was a similar rescue.

"Capt. Dick Willsie was piloting a P-38 over Romania when he had both engines disabled by flak. He crash landed in a field. One of his compatriots, Dick Andrews, landed his P-38 and squeezed Willsie into the single seat cockpit and saved him from certain capture or death.

"Now, on the day of the rescue at A Shau, Willsie was the commander of the 602nd Air Commando Squadron to which Myers was assigned. Dick Andrews was flying top cover during the rescue." The old man held out his coffee cup for a refill. He looked at young Ryan and asked, "Well, what do you think?" Ryan sat in deep thought. "How come this is not in the history books in schools?" The old man smiled and shook his head and said, "it was an unpopular war, and we lost. It is as simple as that." Jesse got up, signaling it was time to go. "Well Colonel, see ya' next time." Elder just nodded and said, "Anytime, Anyplace." Jesse responded, "Anytime Anyplace." Ryan thanked the old man for the story and said goodbye. Elder just smiled and said, "next time bring those boys of yours; we'll make pilots out of them yet." He chuckled.

Bernard Fisher was the first airman to receive the Medal of Honor in the Vietnam Conflict.

Bernard Fisher's Medal of Honor citation reads as follows:

For conspicuous gallantry and intrepidity at the risk of his life above and beyond the call of duty. On that date, the special forces camp at A Shau was under attack by 2,000 North Vietnamese Army regulars. Hostile troops had positioned themselves between the airstrip and the camp. Other hostile troops had surrounded the camp and were continuously raking it with automatic weapons fire from the surrounding hills. The tops of the 1,500 ft hills were obscured by an 800 ft. ceiling, limiting aircraft maneuverability and forcing pilots to operate within range of hostile gun positions, which often were able to fire down on attacking aircraft. During the battle Maj. Fisher observed a fellow airman crash land on the battle torn airstrip. In the belief that the downed pilot was seriously injured and in imminent danger of capture, Maj. Fisher announced his intention to land on the airstrip to affect a rescue. Although aware of the extreme danger and likely failure of such an attempt, he elected to continue. Directing his own air cover, he landed his aircraft and taxied almost the full length of the runway, which was littered with battle debris and parts of an exploded aircraft. While effecting a successful rescue of the downed pilot, heavy ground fire was observed, with 19 bullets striking his aircraft.

Martin

In the face of the withering ground fire, he applied power and gained enough speed to lift off at the overrun of the airstrip. Maj. Fisher's profound concern for his fellow airman, and at the risk of his life above and beyond the call of duty, are in the highest traditions of the United States Air Force and reflect great credit upon himself and the Armed Forces of his country.

Martin

Photo by, USAF photo

#4

of the

Sagas of the Air Commandos

The Story of Para Rescue

The bravest men I ever knew.

The clock on the wall measured the passage of time. Elder stared at it and wondered how much longer he had. He was 94, his career as an Air Force pilot had defined him. He was in this nursing home now because he could not take care of his basic necessities. Outside the light was bright on a sunny southern afternoon. All in all, it was not so bad. He had his books, his TV, and a regular visitor. Could be worse. About this time there was a knock on the door and a raspy voice asking "How ya' doing, Colonel?" The old man looked up to see who it was. It was CMSgt. Taylor from down the hall. Taylor had been a loadmaster; he had never had the old man as an Aircraft Commander, but they both knew the ins and outs of Special Operations. "Never better" retorted Elder, "what about you?" "Oh, you know, it's a fine day to die," he replied. The old man looked outside, smiled, and said, "yes, yes it is." CMSgt Taylor came into the room and asked if he wanted to go outside. The old man was happy to hear him ask because it was hard for him to take himself, and the room was starting to close in on him. The two men made their way down the hall with Taylor pushing Elder in his wheel chair.

It took a while but they made it out onto the veranda and found a shady spot. Taylor parked the old man's wheelchair and found a nice comfy chair for himself.

Elder took a deep breath, smelling deeply the scent of the deep south. In his younger days he had been amazed at how much southern Mississippi and Louisiana looked and smelled like Southeast Asia. Vietnam's delta was just like this.

Elder hadn't flown an airplane in years and it had been five years since he had even been inside of one. But airplanes were part of the old man and CMSgt Taylor. Their memories revolved around missions and people they had known or flown with or had rescued. The old man and CMSgt Taylor made small talk and the topic of conversation got around to, as it usually did, missions they had flown. They talked about daring pilots and loadmasters until CMSgt. Taylor asked the old man who the bravest man was that he ever knew. Elder did not miss a beat and said, "Bill Pitsenbarger." Taylor looked at the Old Man and asked, "what about Dwayne Hackney?" The Old Man looked at Taylor and said, "well he was the most decorated Airman in the entire Vietnam war. He did do some amazing things; but let's look at what Pitsenbarger did.

"He flew 250 missions and on one of them he had to hang on the end of the rescue cable to save a Vietnamese from a burning mine field. His job was to save people and he did it every day. He ended up paying the ultimate price to save other people. When a man knowingly sacrifices his life for the benefit of others, especially someone he does not know, he has to be the bravest of the brave. There may be someone out there of equal bravery, but none braver." CMSgt Taylor asked the old man if he knew about the battle that claimed Pitsenbarger's life.

Elder thought about it and said, "You know, I don't know a lot about it; it was an Army operation and we did not have a lot of tac air involved." Taylor looked pensive and said, "that is right, it was Army and I did some research on it awhile back just to pass some time. It was a really screwed up situation. It all started with Operation Abilene." The old man held up his hand and then said, "This sounds like a long story, how about a cup?" CMSgt Taylor stopped talking, and said, "you're right about that, and I will have a cup." They proceeded back to the old man's room and made a pot of coffee and got out a pint bottle of whiskey. They poured the coffee from the coffee pot on the dresser and settled in for a long afternoon.

After a couple of sips of coffee, CMSgt. Taylor continued. "Well Operation Abilene was a Search and Destroy mission of the 1st Infantry Division. The commander of the Division was a Major General."

"He, like all of the big brass, thought that if you could corner the VC you could wipe them out. That was true; the problem was, we didn't know where the VC were and they were not going to get cornered. Well, the general thought he knew more than anyone so he hatched a plan. Now Operation Abilene was just like any other Search and Destroy mission until the general came up with his plan. His plan was to take Charlie Company, a rifle company, and send them into an area suspected of harboring VC and use them as bait. Hopefully they would make contact with the dreaded D800 battalion and then the general would send in the other rifle companies and wipe them out. As with most of the horse hockey that came out of headquarters, this looked good on paper. What the planners of this little snafu couldn't see was the terrain and jungle conditions that existed between Saigon and Vung Tau. So, they split up their forces and sent these boys out into the jungle to play." The old man was drinking his coffee and listening to CMSgt. Taylor and then spoke up.

Martin

"Well, it doesn't really sound like a bad plan. What was wrong with it?" Taylor continued, "Well, it did look good on paper, but, and this is a big but, Charlie Company was not at full strength. Because of wounded, leave and sickness, they were down to 134 men. They were usually at 150.

They sent these boys out into the field so that they effectively cut themselves off from their sister companies because of terrain and Jungle. If you got ambushed, there was no calvary coming to the rescue. So, Charlie Company was the bait. The farther into the countryside they moved, the more cut off they were from Alpha and Bravo companies. They had moved out on April 10, 1966. The next day as they were moving through the Courtenay Rubber Plantation, they started receiving VC sniper fire. The sniper fire allowed the VC to maneuver around the outnumbered Charlie Company. By 2 o'clock in the afternoon, VC officers were spotted directing the placement of their troops surrounding the Americans.

"It was clear now that the VC had been fooled and had taken the bait. What was also clear is that nobody had thought out the end game. Alpha and Bravo companies could not come to the rescue because of the terrain and the thick jungle.

"Charlie Company realized what was happening and formed up a circular defensive position. The battle of Xa Cam My had begun.

Charlie Company tried to call in an Artillery fire mission on the enemy and the rounds came in on their own position instead. Their situation got worse as time went by. Charley Company called in rescue helicopters to medevac the wounded. The rescue choppers arrived and Bill Pitsenbarger went down the cable and started to assist the wounded. He was able to get six wounded men on the lift to the choppers. The helicopters, under heavy enemy fire, had to leave and come back for another load. Pitsenbarger elected to stay on the ground and take care of the wounded. When the choppers returned, they were engulfed in enemy small arms fire. They had to pull out and Pitsenbarger waved them off. He had elected to stay with Charlie Company. He then began to take care of the wounded and to fight the enemy. He spent hours crawling around in the Jungle looking for wounded soldiers, he would find them and drag them back to the center of the American defenses. Even though he was wounded himself he continued to take care of others. When the soldiers got low on ammo, Pits would gather ammo from the dead and distribute it to them.

"He cared for the wounded and directly fought the VC when he could. The fighting continued through the day and into the night. The VC were aggressive and continued to attack. Charlie Company used everything it had to fight off the attacks. Pitsenbarger was killed by a sniper sometime in the early hours.

All through the night the VC would send small units to breach Charlie Company's defenses. They would breach the defenses and retrieve their own dead and wounded and kill any American wounded they found. It was a terrifying night for Charlie Company. The enemy disengaged by seven o'clock the next morning. They disappeared before the American reinforcements could arrive. Bill Pitsenbarger was found with a M16 rifle in one hand and his medical kit in the other. He did not make it, but nine others did, in no small part, because of his actions. That's why I think that Bill Pitsenbarger was the bravest man I know of. Of course, nothing ever happened to the general that set the whole fiasco up. I don't remember air strikes or any kind of help for Charley Company. They were used as bait and then abandoned by poor planning.

"As it happened in Xa Cam My, Kam Duc, and countless other battles, we lost good soldiers and airmen because of gross incompetence of the people running things." The old man and CMSgt. Taylor were thoughtful for a moment and the old man finally spoke.

"You know he was the youngest airman to ever be awarded the Medal of Honor." CMSgt. Taylor just stared out of the window and asked, "where do we find them, young men who can put someone's life completely ahead of their own?"

Elder reached for the coffee pot for refills and said, "the same place they found us." The old loadmaster looked out of the window and said "You may be right about that; you may be right." The old CMSgt. looked around at Elder and said, "I still think that Dwayne Hackney had the right stuff." "Well," the old man answered, "I will have to agree with you that he was a very special man. He was the most decorated airman of the entire Vietnam War. Some of his exploits made it seem that he had a guardian angel with him all the time." Taylor grunted and said, "I'll say. He hadn't been in Vietnam six months and he was already well respected as a PJ and they TDY'd him from Danang in Vietnam to NKP Thailand flying on Jolly Green Giant rescue helicopters.

"One of their Forward Air Controllers or FAC's had been shot down over a rough patch in Laos. They launched to pick him up at about ten in the morning because a fighter pilot had made radio contact and he was alive and wanting to come home. Everyone knew that you did not want to be shot down over Laos. The Jolly Green that Hackney was on flew into the valley, made contact with the pilot and went to his last known location. Hackney jumped on the penetrator and was lowered into the jungle.

"Hackney found footprints but could not find the pilot. He got back aboard the helicopter and they could not contact the pilot and had to break off the rescue. The crew was on standby back at NKP when, at about 4:30 in the afternoon, another fighter pilot picked up a message from the downed pilot. The Jolly Green and crew launched immediately to go rescue the pilot. They reached the area before dark but bad weather had settled in.

"Two Sandy attack aircraft were in the area and in contact with the downed pilot, but, and this is a big but, they could not fly into the valley to protect the helicopter because the mountains were hidden by overcast. The crew of the Jolly Green talked about the situation and the entire crew voted to go after the pilot without escort. The Jolly Green was able to raise the pilot on the radio.

"Two Jolly Greens went in, one to effect the rescue and a second one to fly high backup. The downed airman seemed to be in good spirits and not badly injured. He was able to direct the helicopter to his location. Hackney went down the cable to get him and in three minutes the pilot of the Jolly Green radioed that the pilot was aboard. Back at NKP the downed pilot's FAC friends were all in operations listening to the radio and a cheer went up when they heard the news.

"The cheers were short lived, as the Jolly Green pulled out under heavy fire. They were raked with a burst of 37mm Anti-aircraft fire. When Hackney had brought the pilot into the helicopter, they started taking heavy enemy fire. Hackney took his parachute and put it on the rescued pilot. He then made his way to the back and grabbed another parachute and put his arms through the harness. The Jolly Green pilot radioed 'we've been hit, we've been hit'. It was just then that a burst of 37mm had hit the aircraft in the middle, causing severe damage and a very serious fire. It was this second hit that blew Dwayne Hackney out of his helicopter. Hackney did not have the parachute on yet, just his arms through the harness, and, he was only a couple of hundred feet above the ground.

"It was by instinct alone that he pulled the D ring that opened the parachute. The chute was still opening when he hit the trees and it left him hanging a few feet above the ground. He climbed down and made his way over to some of the wreckage of his helicopter. Being out of control it had crashed into the rock ledge and exploded. The high bird of the two-helicopter package came down and rescued Hackney, they found no sign of any other survivors.

"Hackney was badly burned and in shock from the experience and passed out on his way to the hospital in NKP. He was awarded the Air Force Cross for his actions that day, putting his responsibility to his survivor above that of his own life. You know, usually a feat of heroism is a one-off event, but not with Hackney; it seemed to happen to him all the time." The old man said. "Yeah, we all heard about that mission, but how does one end up with 70 decorations and not be dead?" "Well," said CMSgt. Taylor, "In Hackney's case, you just keep coming to work every day.

"Several weeks later, two marine troop transport helicopters went down just south of the DMZ and two Jolly Green Giant rescue helicopters were deployed to go get the survivors.

"Hackney was part of the crew of one of those birds. The crash site was on the side of a mountain with jungle so thick that you had to lower the rescue cable its full length, over two hundred feet, to reach the ground. Coming back up the cable from his last descent, the pilots report said 'bullets began to pepper the aircraft like popcorn popping'.

"He was rotated home and stationed in California. Hackney was a celebrity. He made the rounds of talk shows, including, The Tonight Show with Johnny Carson and The Ed Sullivan Show. He spent Christmas of 1967 in Monaco as the guest of Prince Rainier and Princess Grace. When they gave him his Air Force Cross for his action of putting his parachute on his survivor, they also gave him a silver star for his actions on the ground during a rocket attack at Da Nang . And after all of this attention, what did Dwayne Hackney do? He volunteered to go back to Vietnam. This guy was a little crazy." The old man looked up at this and said, "look who's talking; how many tours did you do?" The CMSgt. Looked kind of sheepish and said, "three, how about you?" The old man grinned and counted on his fingers, and then said, "four, total." He then looked at the CMSgt. and said. "Go on, I just wanted to make sure I know what makes a man crazy."

They both laughed and the CMSgt. continued with the story. "Well, Hackney went back to Vietnam in 1970 and started flying rescue missions again. North Vietnam, South Vietnam and Laos were all covered. It was in Laos that his next close call came. It seems that four South Vietnamese soldiers were in Laos and had gotten trapped by the enemy and Hackney and his Jolly Green Giant crew were dispatched to go get them out. There were three Jolly Greens in the package.

"Heavy ground fire stopped the first attempt at lowering a penetrator. Hackney, seeing the angle of the side of the mountain, suggested, a low hover and he and his fellow PJ's could just pull them into the helicopter. Now, this is teamwork. The way I heard it, Hackney lay down in the door and his partner PJ straddled him to keep him in the chopper. Hackney would pull the Vietnamese up far enough for his buddy to pull them inside.

"The big helicopters had miniguns and were exchanging heavy fire with the enemy. The engine was hit and they went down. One of our Sandy's was shot down in the same exchange. The other Jolly Green picked them up.

"Hackney had been hit in the head, and was having trouble standing and walking. Petty, his partner, was hit directly with a 51 Cal and had most of the back of his bicep blown away. The PJ's insisted that the wounded be taken to the army hospital in Da Nang. They were not so quick to amputate. Petty survived and kept his arm. Hackney had a bullet hole in his helmet. The bullet had entered the front of the helmet, had grazed his scalp and followed the contour of the helmet and exited the back. Now you tell me that this guy did not have a guardian angel." The old man and the CMSgt. refilled their coffee cups and added a little taste of bourbon.

The CMSgt. told the old man how lucky he was to have a friend that visited regularly and would bring him a little contraband. The old man just smirked and said "Yeah, Jesse was the best loadmaster I ever had." The CMSgt. said, "Well, one of these days, you are going to have to tell me about some of the things you two got into." The old man looked up and said, "I may do that, but right now, I'd like to hear what happened to Hackney." The CMSgt. took a sip and started back with his story. "Oh yeah, well, after Vietnam he got out of the Air Force for four years. He was a sheriff's deputy back in his home town. Not surprisingly, he was bored.

Martin

"Four years later he had the opportunity to get back in the Air Force as an E-4 and he jumped right on it. He made his rank back quick enough and qualified to be an instructor PJ. He served with Special Ops forces all over the world and finally ended up in England in 1980. One of his last missions as a PJ was to rescue two Brits who got into trouble while mountain climbing in Wales. Of the injuries he suffered on that rescue was a fractured skull and a broken hip. In 1981 he had a heart attack that ended his PJ days forever.

"Hackney was re-assigned to Scott AFB and put in Intelligence. It was here that he met a young girl named Carole who would become his wife.

"The funny thing is, she had no idea who Duane Hackney was, and only found out while studying for her own promotion test. To say that Hackney did not talk about his exploits would be an understatement. They had a son; I think he would have been born in 1984. Hackney did not like the intelligence field; he cross-trained into the Security Police in 1985. He was assigned to Sawyer AFB, a SAC base, and became the First SGT of the Security Police squadron. He was First SGT of the Year for the Eighth Air Force in 1987. Hackney was a CMSgt. when he retired in 1991.

"He moved his family to Williamsport, Pa. and built a new home in nearby Trout Run. He entered college and was studying to be a nurse anesthetist. He was in his second semester when he had another heart attack and died. He was 46 years old.

"They say the funeral home in his home town of Flint was packed for three days and the funeral procession was five miles long. Yeah, I think Dwayne Hackney was the bravest man I know." The old man rubbed his chin thoughtfully and said, "You know, the problem is that stories like that are in every rescue squadron and I would go as far to say that every PJ had done something notable."
"Well," said the CMSgt. "I think you are right about that.

"Did you ever hear about Charley Smith? He and his whole crew just threw it in the North Vietnamese's faces."
"What did they do?" asked the old man. "Well," said the CMSgt.," they were staging with Jolly Greens up in Laos on the North Vietnamese border at a Lima site waiting for an F-105 strike north of Hanoi to be over. It all looked good and they were ready to go home for the night when one of the 105's got tagged pretty good on the way out. They heard the exchange on the radio from the pilot and knew he was going down, so they launched into North Vietnam.

Martin

"The pilot during this time was riding this airborne bomb so he could get on the south side of the Red River. Everyone knew that if you went down north of the Red River, they would not come for you. The pilot's name was Sparks, if you can believe that, and his plane was on fire so bad that other planes kept calling in SAM sightings. He rode it. He had to blow the canopy to clear the smoke out of the cockpit. One of his rudder pedals melted off. There was fire in the cockpit and he just kept going toward the river. He rode it until it just wouldn't fly anymore. As it entered a flat spin, Sparks ejected. The ejection went well, except for the risers beating his face, he looked up and had a good canopy. He steered away from villages that he could see and finally landed in a bamboo thicket. He got beat up pretty bad on the landing but, all in all, he was OK.

"Meanwhile, Charley Smith and his crew were on their way. Smith's Aircraft Commander that day was Captain Harry Walker. As they were making their way to Sparks, they were ordered over the radio to turn back. They were told to abort the mission; Sparks was too far north and the risk was too great. Walker checked with his crew and then answered that he could not hear them and they were proceeding with the mission. The Sandy's, A1-E Skyraiders, got to Sparks first.

"This was a really hot area right in the enemy's back yard. The enemy was mobilizing to come and capture the pilot. And, and this is a big, there are Migs in the area. With Sandy's in the area, Sparks' fighter buddies had headed home. The Sandy's had Sparks on the radio and had marked his position. They then proceeded to mark with smoke two areas well away from the pilot. Sparks got on the radio to tell them that they were marking the wrong place and the Sandy's pilot quickly let him know that it was planned and that they knew what they were doing. It was a standard technique to lure the enemy in the wrong direction.

"Besides knives, guns and radios, the Air Force had smartly given all aircrew pen flares. It was going to be this pen flare that let the Jolly Green know his exact position. The Jolly Green came in and Sparks sent up a flare. Smith called out that he saw him, and they hovered as Smith started to let down the penetrator. It was about this time that four Mig 17's showed up. Someone kept screaming on the radio for the Jolly Green to get out. Captain Walker, famously replied, "F--- you, I have more important things to do." The Jolly Green is a big helicopter, and it is in a hover. It was a sitting duck if there ever was one. The Migs rolled in and made a fire run at over 300 mph.

"They fired a missile but they had waited too long and the missile never got a lock on the helicopter. The missile flew past the Jolly Green and exploded into a hillside in the distance. That was the only missile they fired. They must have had the Sandy's on radar and thought that other fighters were in the area. To everyone's relief, they rolled out. The penetrator went down and Sparks got on. They reeled him into the cargo compartment and started giving him medical treatment. The Sandy's escorted them as they hightailed it back to Laos.

"Charley Smith was also the PJ who went in after Karl Richter. "I heard about that," said the old man. "It was his 198th mission." "Yeah, said the CMSgt. "They found him and Smith went down to get him. He said he could hear the enemy all around him as he put Richter in the Stokes basket. But he had fallen down a cliff and he was dead when Smith got to him; A sad tale, but true." The two men took another break and an orderly came in to give each man his afternoon meds. They did not say much until the orderly had left. The old man poured the rest of his whiskey into the two coffee cups and emptied the coffeepot into them. "Sgt. Taylor," said the old man, "you know, you and I never crewed a plane together, but we have flown the same types of missions in the same areas of the world.

Martin

"Everyone looks at those old cargo aircraft and think we are just truck drivers." "Well yeah," said the CMSgt. "No one knew what our mission was, so they left us alone; I liked that part of it." "Me too," said the old man. "And we flew some hellish missions, all over the world. But, those rescue guys, the PJ's, they were the bravest men I ever knew. We flew into hell once in a while, but they flew into it every day. They went on alert and waited for a life-threatening mission to come up. And they would come and get you, no matter what, no matter how bad it was. You just can't give them enough credit. And it was the PJ's who were the driving force.

"I have heard many complaints from them that their pilots would not go get someone because it was too hot. They looked on that pilot like he was a coward. My loadmaster was like that. One time we had an airdrop scheduled and headquarters wanted to cancel the drop, so I went to the crew and asked them what they wanted to do.

"The co-pilot and the engineer said it was up to me and do you know what my loadmaster said to me?" The CMSgt shook his head. "He looked at me and told me I was getting paid to take him and his cargo to the drop point, and he and his cargo were ready to go, so what are we waiting for?

111

Martin

"I was stunned; no one on any of my crews had ever talked to me that way. And he was dead serious. I was looking right into his eyes and he never flinched, I looked at the rest of the crew and said, 'Well, let's saddle up and ride'. And we did. We made the drop, took fourteen hits and when we got back the loadmaster looked at me and said, 'That was some pretty good flying.' All I could say was 'thanks' and he walked off the plane." "You know," said CMSgt. Taylor, "I wish I had flown with you; we would have had a good time." "You may be right, that guy was the last loadmaster I ever had. I was making a report to the squadron commander and he asked me how my new loadmaster was doing. I told him he was a little wild, but probably the best loadmaster in the theater." The CMSgt. finished his coffee and asked, "that isn't the guy who comes to see you every week is it?" The old man, looked up with a twinkle in his eye. "One and the same."

Airman Pitsenbargers' Medal of Honor Citation reads as follows.

On April 11, 1966, near Cam My, Republic of Vietnam, A1C Pitsenbarger sacrificed his life to save nine others. He was a pararescue man on a helicopter evacuating American casualties from a dense jungle area, and voluntarily organized and coordinated rescue efforts at the scene, ensuring that the recovery operation proceeded smoothly. However, when the last wounded person had been assisted to the recovery site, the hovering rescue helicopter was hit by enemy fire and the pilot was forced to make an emergency landing at an airstrip nearby, abandoning rescue attempts. A1C Pitsenbarger volunteered to stay behind and tend to the wounded amid heavy mortar and sniper fire.He continually exposed himself to intensive automatic fire while collecting weapons from fallen comrades for use by remaining defenders. Even after he'd been incapacitated by his wounds, A1C Pitsenbarger continued directing defensive efforts. His actions during the mission were initially recognized with a posthumous award of the Air Force Cross. That award is the military's second-highest for service members, and the highest award the Air Force can bestow.

Upon further review in the 1990s, a number of private citizens and government officials lobbied successfully to have the citation upgraded to the Medal of Honor

Photo by, USAF photo

Dwayne Hackney received 70 medals. He was the most decorated Airman in the Vietnam War.

#5

of the

Sagas of the Air Commandos

How We Lost Phou Pha Thi

or

The Fall of Lima Site 85

On a cold, crisp, southern winter morning, the Colonel, or the old man, as everyone called him behind his back, was sitting in a wheelchair on the porch of his nursing home, watching the sun rise. As the light flooded around him, he smiled to himself and thought it was a fine day to die. He was enjoying a cup of coffee that the night orderly had brought to him. This was a nursing home for veterans, so he knew that he would be joined soon by others looking to enjoy the early morning. Today would be a good day for the old man. Today he would get a visitor, a man he had flown combat missions with who came every Tuesday and Thursday when he could. He and the old man would reminisce about things they had done and other people had done. Sometimes they would be joined by the man's son and grandsons, and sometimes an irascible old CMSgt. that lived down the hall. All good folks, Elder enjoyed their company. He stayed out on the porch until they came to get him for breakfast.

The orderly wanted to push him in, but, the old man shooed him away and tried to push himself. He was not going to give up on one of the few things he could still do for himself. The dining room was light and airy. There were table cloths on the tables and the kitchen staff brought out the food and served them.

Martin

It was a far cry from the chow halls of the Air Force,
but he remembered a British chow hall on Akritiri Island
that looked just like this and they had enlisted men serving
the food. That place was for officers only, but, the old man
had told them that his crew ate together, so either seat the
entire crew or we would find other accommodations. They
seated the entire crew. After breakfast he pushed himself
down the hall to his room. An orderly came in to help him
with his meds and to use the bathroom. He had the young
man help him into a shirt that his visitor had given to him
for Christmas. He flipped on the news on his TV and waited.

Jesse was 69 and was driving to see his old aircraft
commander. He went to see him twice a week when it was
possible. He enjoyed these visits as much as the old man
did. Three people that he knew had died in the last two
weeks. People die, so he knew these visits would not last
forever. Elder was 94 years old and holding. Jesse often
thought about how long it had been since the war. He and
the old man would suit up in the mornings for a great
adventure. It had been well over a half a century and the
marks it had left on them were still clearly evident. These
visits were important to them both.

Jesse pulled into the parking lot of the nursing home and into one of the handicapped parking places. His back and his knees were acting up a little bit today. He got out of the car, retrieved his cane and headed for the entrance. Entering the lobby, he passed the Aviary where the parakeets were singing and went to the nurse's station.

Tricia, the head nurse, was at the desk and smiled at Jesse as he approached. He checked in with Tricia every time he came. "How is the old man today?" asked Jesse, and Tricia just smiled and said, "About the same. What kind of trouble are you two going to get into today?" "Trouble," said Jesse. "Yes, you know we can smell those coffee cups of yours, and we have a good idea of where he gets the whiskey," she replied. Jesse looked up with an innocent look on his face and said. "It must be that old CMSgt. down the hall." She looked at him with a knowing grin and said, "yeah that must be it." "Well, thank you, I'll see you later," he said as he turned to go down the hall to the old man's room. He could feel the pint of Bourbon in his coat pocket and smiled to himself knowing that the old man would get a kick out of it. Two solid raps on the open doorjamb and a "How's it going, Colonel?" brought the old man back to the present and he answered, "never better."

As Jesse took off his coat to get more comfortable, he pulled out the pint of Jack Daniels whiskey and handed it to the old man. Elder handed the bottle back to him and said, "would you put that in the drawer for me?" "Sure," said Jesse as he took the bottle and walked over to the old man's dresser. The second drawer pulled out like any other drawer. Jesse pushed it back in and reached on both sides to press small clips. When he pulled the drawer back out, it left the large top portion of the drawer and exposed a smaller space on the bottom. In that space was another whiskey bottle with about a third left, a combat knife, and a small pistol, just in case the Russians or the Chinese or somebody would attack the nursing home. There would be hell to pay if the nursing home ever found out about it, but, the old man wanted it, so Jesse got it for him. There were a few other odds and ends as Jesse placed the full bottle and retrieved the used one. He then slid the drawer shut and reopened it, as a normal drawer.

It came out looking like a regular drawer. No one knew of this except the old man and Jesse. Jesse had made the dresser with the secret compartments for the old man. The old man looked at the large envelope that Jesse had brought with him and asked, "Is that what we needed for last time?"

Martin

"Yes, it is. This is the CIA report and the Air Force CHECO report." "How in the world did you get those?" asked the old man incredulously. "On the internet. A lot of this stuff has been declassified. A lot of stuff is online, and if it is, you don't even have to request it. I can search the CIA online files and download and print whatever I want." The old man took the files and said. "I am surprised they let this out; it has to make them look bad." "Oh yeah, just like we thought. I am going down to get Sgt. Taylor; he was real interested in this," said Jesse. The old man was going through the papers that Jesse had brought. "By all means; besides, you and he speak the same language." "I'll be right back," was the reply. And with that Jesse walked out of the old man's room and went down the hall looking for an old loadmaster named CMSgt. Taylor. He found him in his room and invited him down to the old man's and Taylor was delighted to accept. Jesse and CMSgt. Taylor came back into the old man's room and Jesse put on a pot of coffee. Elder was ready. "What do you know about Lima site 85 Taylor?" Sgt Taylor looked at Jesse and the old man and said, "I only know two things about it. One, CMSgt. Etchberger's Air Force Cross was just upgraded to the Medal of Honor, and two, it was one of the biggest screw ups in the entire war."

Elder looked up and said, "You are right about that; take a look at these." He then handed the papers to Taylor. CMSgt. Taylor looked at them and said, "Wow!" That was all he needed to say. The old man took the papers back and said, "let's start with what we know. A Lima site had nothing to do with the United States Air Force. Remember this is Laos, and in 1967 when all of this took place, Laos is a neutral country but, and this is the big but, it is in the middle of a civil war. The communist Pathet Lao controls the northern part of the country and the U.S. is supporting the anticommunists. These are being led by General Vang Pao and his Hmong freedom fighters. The military cannot have a presence there so the CIA is running the counter insurgency and supplying General Vang Pao. A Lima Site, and there were hundreds of them, was just an airstrip out in the boonies where the CIA could land and resupply Vang Pao's troops. Lima Site 85 was just such a strip that happened to be near a place called Phou Pha Thi. It was also the home of a rock that jutted 1,600 feet straight up, with sheer cliffs on three sides and an almost impenetrable fourth side. Since we were flying into North Vietnam every day, the Air Force had had the CIA put a TACAN on top of what the Americans called 'The Rock'.

"A TACAN is just a navigational beacon. Planes coming out of the north from bombing missions could use it to find their way home. The Pathet Lao and their North Vietnamese partners did not pay too much attention to the TACAN because it would be way more trouble than it was worth to try to take it. So all is well until some brainiac general decided that we should have all weather bombing in the north and we should install a TSQ-81 COMBAT SKYPOT radar bomb scoring system. This would allow them to control bombing missions in all weather conditions and improve accuracy. The top of The Rock was flat enough for the radar, the TACAN and a few buildings. There was a helicopter pad down a path from the top about a quarter of a mile from the radar site; it was used to bring in technicians and fuel for the TACAN generator. The Rock was resupplied weekly by an Air Commando unit out of Udorn, Thailand. There would be a need for a lot more technicians and supplies with the TSQ-81. The problem was that all of the technicians were military and they were not allowed in a neutral country.

"The Prime Minister of Laos, Souphanna Phucat, had agreed to the Radar as long as he did not know about it. Ambassador Sullivan thought that that would be OK as long as all of the decisions about the site came through him.

"The 7th Air Force in Saigon agreed to that. Since everyone in charge had made a decision, it was time to figure out how to do it. It was Special Operations that came up with the plan; it was the 7th Air Force that screwed it up. It was time to get some military civilians. The CIA had Air America and did control the military actions in the area but they did not have the technicians needed. Since the Air Force was the only user of the TSQ-81 radar, they had the only available technicians. So, we sheep dipped them."

"I have heard of that," said CMSgt. Taylor. "Exactly what is that?" "Well", said the old man, "you get volunteers for a specific mission or job and ask if they would be willing to be a civilian while they were doing it. If they say yes, then they are discharged from the service.

"They go do the job, and are reenlisted when they get back, and it's like they never left." Taylor looked at Jesse and the old man and said, "I have heard of it, but never got close to it, how about you guys?" The old man just grinned and looked at Jesse and asked, "Where was your first discharge located?" Jesse looked at Elder and Taylor and said, "Phan Rang Air Base, Vietnam." The old man grinned and looked at Taylor and said. "I have one of those too."

Taylor looked amazed and asked, "what did you all do?" The old man held up his hand and said, "That is a story for another day. For now, let's get back to Phou Pha Thi. The Air Force conducted interviews with the volunteers until they had a group they could use. They even interviewed the wives so there would be no misunderstanding and no breaching of security. So, we had this group of volunteers, including CMSgt. Richard L. Etchberger. The code name for the operation was Heavy Green.

"All of these airmen would be discharged from the Air Force and given credentials to show they worked for Lockheed Aircraft. Dressed in civilian clothes they were sent to Udorn Air Base in Thailand. That is where they lived, and on paper that is where they worked. They were sent to Lima site 85 on one and two-day shifts, and then they would be replaced. They set up the radar and other small buildings to eat and sleep in. Remember now, the command post with their radio communications was a quarter of a mile away, down by the helicopter pad." The old man was frowning because it was obvious how stupid this plan was. "So now what do we have?" The old man was agitated. "A secret military radar in a neutral country, allowed by the Prime Minister with a wink and a nod.

"I don't know why people kept calling it secret; everyone in Southeast Asia knew it was there. The Thai's, the Laotians, the Pathet Lao, the North Vietnamese, the 7th Air Force and everyone else that could read a map. Remember, there was already a TACAN there. Plus, and this is a big one, they had relinquished all decisions about the place to the Laotian Ambassador, Sullivan." The old man looked at his buddies and said. "there have never been better makings for a SNAFU than this." Jesse and CMSgt. Taylor were reading through the documents and they were verifying everything the old man had been telling them. He had researched Lima Site 85 many years ago and remembered every detail. The old man asked for another cup of coffee and took a little break. CMSgt. Taylor looked up from the CIA report and said, "So, we moved men and material onto The Rock until we had a bombing control radar up and running. We were moving a team of 12 men every one or two days to the top of the rock via the helipad down from the top. All this had been set and was running by November, 1967. The Air Force must have loved it, being able to hit bombing targets even in bad weather."

The old man looked up and said, "Sure they did, it made them look like they knew what they were doing. But that also made them turn a blind eye to the intel that was coming in about the area around Phou Pha Thi. Everyone knew the CIA was running the war in Laos. Their airline, Air America, did all of the resupply and rescue in Laos. They were paying Vang Pao and his Hmong army and directing them against the Pathet Lao. There are unsubstantiated rumors that Air America was even involved in the Opium trade to help fund all of these operations. But that being said, they had good solid intel. They reported that intel in a timely manner. The 7th Air Force knew what was going on in the surrounding area and what was coming." Jesse looked up from his copy of the paperwork and sipped from his coffee cup. "It looks like it was fairly obvious what was happening," he said. "It was," replied the old man who was totally involved in the story now.

"The Pathet Lao and the North Vietnamese had noticed the increased activity on the top of The Rock. Helicopters were delivering more equipment and men and flights were now in and out every day. They knew about the radar." "How did they know that?" asked CMSgt. Taylor.

The old man slowly shook his head. "Well," he said slowly, "when you are operating a counter insurgency, you have to use indigenous people. When you do that, there is always a fringe of those troops that are playing for both sides." The old man finished his coffee and started in again. "The CIA, doing their job, had been reporting troop buildup and road construction in the area. Now the rainy season was ending, so the enemy could continue its preparations. The CIA rightly judged that they were building roads to attack Phou Pha Thi. The construction continued on Route 19 from Dien Bien Phu to Nam Bac and along Route 6 to Phou Pha Thi. This could only be the setup for an offensive.

"Understand this," said Elder. "This is Karst Jungle territory; you cannot move large numbers of troops and supplies without roads. The North Vietnamese nor the Pathet Lao had any form of air transport like we did. Knowing that the Vietnamese and the Pathet Lao only started offenses in the dry season, the CIA had this thing pegged right from the start. If only someone had been listening." The old man shook his head. He then leaned back in his chair like they would be there for a while and began again. "The Communists began their offensive in early December.

"They started by sending out small units to harass our lines and to test our defenses. By December 15, 1967 Hmong recon patrols and CIA lookouts detected several battalions moving against Nam Bac. Now considering a battalion has 300 to 800 men in it, what we have here is a major troop movement. Nam Bac is a very important stronghold for the Royal Lao Army. At the same time, they were moving toward Phou Pha Thi.

"The Pathet Lao took Phou Den Din, which was only 12 Kilometers away from Phou Pha Thi, on the 16th. Vang Pao's Hmong troops recovered that position later in the day, but it was just a harbinger for things to come. The CIA knew that we needed to focus on the security of the radar site and the enemy's determination to take it.

"As massed columns of enemy showed up and apparently encircled the site, we had to do something, so we started hitting them with air strikes. We hit them with F-4's and F-105's. Now, you all know how ineffective fast movers are in the jungle, and this situation was no exception. So, we started bringing in A-1E strikes from Thailand and Vietnam. These were a lot more effective. We even brought in the Nimrods at night. Those were converted B-26's from the big war and were now A-26's.

"By the third of January 1968 we were up to 45 strikes per day. That's an awful lot of air power. We were trying to turn the advances on Highways 19 and 6, but we were only able to weaken it.

"It was at this time that the battle for Nam Bac intensified, and on the 14th of January 1968 it fell to four NVA battalions. There were no survivors and a huge number of documents and other material were captured. Now the boys on top of The Rock, now nicknamed Commando Club, were just hitting their stride. They were controlling 23% of the total strikes against the North. Even as the weather deteriorated, they were able to direct bombing accurately throughout the Hanoi Haiphong complex as well as in the immediate area of Phou Pha Thi for their own defense. This capability gave the Air Force an exaggerated sense of defensibility of the site using air power even though the CIA, the Air Commandos, and Air Force advisors warned of the vulnerability of the site.

Even the Ambassador had serious doubts about the security of the people there. The strategy, as of January, 1968, was to operate the station and the radar to the last minute.

"We would use close air support to keep attackers from reaching the summit while the personnel were evacuated by helicopter. As it says in the CIA report, 'the one contingency not considered proved fatal.'"

Elder, CMSgt. Taylor, and Jesse all sat around going over the paperwork and shaking their heads. "I think they may have been criminally negligent," Jesse said, without looking up. The old man looked at him and said, "Well, let's look at what we have. We have an illegal radar site on top of a mountain in the middle of enemy territory. We are now surrounded by a large enemy force who are moving on the radar site. We have twelve men operating the radar on top of the mountain and they are unarmed.

"And the powers that be think that we can wait until the enemy is almost to the top of the mountain and then just swoop in and evacuate the men with helicopters. The main defense was 200 Hmong who guarded the ridgeline and another 800 who were in the valley below. That sounds good, but these were guerilla fighters, not regular troops. They were ill suited to set up static defenses. They would most likely break and run under attack.

"Up until the 10th of January the NVA and the Pathet Lao probed and mortared the defenses of Phou Pha Thi. On the 10th, the Hmong engaged a Pathet Lao patrol and dispersed it. On the 12th, CIA lookouts reported four planes heading for the mountain. Two of them split off, but, the other two continued on to bomb and strafe the ridgeline."

"These planes were old Soviet Antonov-2 Colt biplanes. Ground fire did not stop the attacks, so the CIA officers on the ground called in a CIA helicopter that was in the area. It was a Bell 212, the civilian version of the Army's Huey. It was faster than the Colts and a crew chief fired at them from the door of the helicopter. He shot down both planes. It is actually in their report that they recovered the rudder of one of the planes and took it back to the Air America base at Longtiang as a souvenir. This attack was unusual; the planes were jury rigged to drop mortar shells as bombs. The Embassy thought the air attack was an attempt to destroy the radar without a costly ground attack. They also considered, and rightly so, that it was unlikely to be repeated. The NVA simply did not have air assets to use in an effective attack. After the air attack, things on the ground started to move quickly.

"On January 19,1968, a CIA informant reported that a five-battalion group of NVA and Pathet Lao had moved west and split into two groups. Three battalions, with a 105-howitzer moved into position to attack Phou Den Din, a key position to controlling the Phou Pha Thi area.

"Two other battalions moved southeast of the mountain in order to encircle the mountain. The CIA and Hmong forces on the mountain recognized another major assault being prepared. They knew then that if the enemy were willing to accept heavy losses, the ridgeline could not be held." The old man paused and Jesse spoke up. "And why are those guys still on that mountain? You and I both know that once that main assault started, you are not going to be able to evacuate the top by helicopter." "That is true," said the old man. "It seems that everyone knew, but nothing was done." The three men looked over the reports in their hands and shook their heads. The old man was reading the CIA report and started reading aloud, "Listen to this, 'at this point, the Air Force personnel manning the radar at the summit were still unarmed and dependent upon orders from the Ambassador to evacuate in the event of a major attack'.

" 'The officers in charge of the detachment that continued to rotate in and out of the site, had no authority to defend their troops or to order an evacuation if the ridge was overrun. Communications with the capitol of Vientiane were maintained from the command post, which was a 20-minute walk from the top of the mountain at the helipad.

" 'The Air Force personnel realized their predicament, but they continued to direct large numbers of airstrikes daily both in Vietnam and Laos. They also began looking for an escape route.' " CMSgt. Taylor had a copy of the CIA report and held up his hand. "That sounds bad, but it gets worse. It says that on January 25th, the people on site conducted a self-defense test that included diverting fighters to suspected enemy positions around Phou Pha Thi. So, the Commando Club conducted its own test and the test indicated that the defense of the site with close air support was unlikely to succeed.

"Now you would think that the generals down at the 7th Air Force would be concerned about the lives of these men, but no, they weren't. They were angry that the test had violated procedure and caused them embarrassment."

There was a pause, and finally Jesse spoke up. "I am so glad that the leadership of the Air Commandos was competent and cared more about the men than about their own careers. The 7th Air Force was looking at the data and forming no opinions." "You know," said the old man, "in my career I have flown hard missions, dangerous missions and some missions that people would say were almost suicide missions. But it was always to help other people. Never just to further my own career."

CMSgt. Taylor held up his copy of the CIA report and said. "After the test and the response from the 7th Air Force, the men on top of Phou Pha Thi developed a plan to descend down the sheer rock face of the mountain on ropes if the major attack came."

CMSgt. Taylor looked up amazed and said. "they were left with their only defense to run and hide in the jungle and hope for rescue." He slammed the report down on his knee and gruffly said, "this is just pissing me off." "Well, you are not alone in that," the old man said. He was ticked off too. "Let's take a break, I could use a cup of coffee, and I need it flavored up." They all nodded and · Jesse went for the bottle and the coffee pot.

After a good long break where everyone got what they needed and used the facilities. The old man had to have orderlies help him and so needed to wait for them to clear out. They then went back to the reports. The old man took the lead. "Okay, so here is where we're at so far. The top of the mountain basically had no defense, save whatever airstrikes were available. Phou Den Din fell on 22 January and the NVA had apparently halted offensive operations to regroup and resupply. They were probably delaying the offensive until more artillery could be brought up.

"During this time, the men on the mountain continued to direct airstrikes on hopefully weakened enemy positions. CIA forward air controllers from Longtiang directed other available missions and the Royal Laotian Air Force helped strike every potential enemy target in range of Phou Pha Thi or more commonly known as Lima Site 85." The old man looked up at his friends and said, "you notice it said potential enemy targets." The men looked at each other and then shook their heads. Jesse spoke up. "So, they had no idea whether they were actually hitting the enemy or not." CMSgt. Taylor and the old man concurred. Elder went back to reading the report.

"It says on January 30th the enemy had detonated some of the mines that had been placed to guard approaches to the American compound. They also brought the ridgeline under mortar fire. The CIA officer sent out a Hmong patrol and they did not meet any serious resistance.

"The commander of Commando Club reported that the action was a 'minor testing of defenses and no further action need be taken'. After the action on January 30th the enemy settled in to a containment perimeter about 12 kilometers in diameter around Phou Pha Thi.

"Engagements between the Hmong and the enemy became infrequent, but, and this is important, the contacts that were made were with enemy formations of at least company strength. This should have sent up red flags everywhere, but it didn't. Just because there were fewer airstrikes for the mountain's defense, the report says that through February 14th there was a sense of confidence at the Embassy in Vientiane and at the 7th Air Force regarding the safety of Site 85. Now this is what really chaps my hide," said Elder. "The CIA report then says 'During this period, there was ample intelligence indicating that the enemy was gradually encircling Phou Pha Thi and massing for a major attack.'

"This information, however, did not materially affect US strategy towards the operation or defense of the site. The Pathet Lao were not hiding their intentions. Numerous informers and spies reported that the enemy planned to take Site 85 in late February. The CIA reported in an estimate on 25 February that it was extremely unlikely that the site could be held beyond 10 March. Still, no significant changes were made to the strategy for defense of Phou Pha Thi and Vientiane retained control of the evacuation plan." The report goes on to say, the casual approach probably was the result of constant air strikes and communications with the site and the continuing practice of rotating men out of it every day or every other day. The planners at the Embassy evidently believed that, in the event that the Commando Clubs' radar bunkers were seriously threatened, the team would be airlifted out and not replaced.

"They may not have realized that the situation could deteriorate rapidly or that a communications breakdown could leave the Commando Club team stranded. The responsibility for the fate of Phou Pha Thi remained at the Embassy and 7th Air Force level. The local commander was never given the authority to order an evacuation or to supervise his own defense."

Martin

Jesse was flipping through his copy of the CIA report and chimed in with, "Look at this." He pointed to a paragraph and read, "In late February the CIA and the Air Force FACS knew the ridgeline was in peril, but they believed it could be defended for the present. On February 18, an NVA officer was killed in an ambush. His captured notebook confirmed a major assault on the summit was planned, gave the strength of the attacking force and described the timing of the attack."

"Oh my God!" gasped Jesse. "They knew everything, the who, the when, and the how. How could you not act on this information and evacuate those men?"

"Oh, they acted on it all right." The old man held up his copy of the report. "On February 21, the Ambassador authorized bombing of all enemy sites. They bombed it every day. Unfortunately, as you know, bombing is pretty ineffective on enemy in the deep jungle. Then on February 26, Ambassador Sullivan wrote to the Air Force Chief of Staff, 'In the final analysis, it seems doubtful that the site can be held in the face of consistent enemy determination. Therefore, we are in touch with the USAF authorities on evacuation and destruction plans. We are fairly certain these can be carried out in an orderly fashion.' "

The old man looked up and said, "As the report goes on to ask, Why, then, was this not done?" The men looked at each other and shook their heads. They knew that the Air Commandos in Thailand and the CIA had gotten together with the Officer in charge of this operation at the Embassy in Vientiane and had a plan.

The plan was that Three Air Commando HH-1 Jolley Green Giant rescue helicopters and two Air America, (CIA) Bell 212 Huey helicopters with a combined capacity of 155 people were to be used. The plan also called for the evacuation of the Hmong guerrillas defending the immediate area of the summit. To provide an immediate response in case of a surprise attack, the two Air America choppers were to remain on alert at nearby Lima Site 98. The Air Force aircraft were to fly from Thailand. The wildcard in the plan was the weather. Low ceilings and visibility, common in northern Laos in March, could keep any aircraft from landing on the tiny mountaintop clearing. The old man, Jesse , and CMSgt. Taylor just looked incredulously at each other. The Old Man spoke first. "We made them Air Commandos without giving them any training." He then looked at Jesse and asked. "If we landed in a hot landing zone and couldn't take off, what would you do?"

Jesse never hesitated. "I would secure our weapons and exit the aircraft to search for a place we could shelter and set up a defensive perimeter." "That's right, and how do you know that?" Elder asked. "That's what we were trained to do," Jesse replied. "That's right," said the old man, "you were trained. Our United States Air Force sent men into a clandestine situation behind enemy lines who did not know how to do anything except run a radar. That brings us to CMSgt. Richard Etchberger; he was the lead enlisted man on that mountaintop, but he wasn't in charge.

"There was an Air Force officer in charge and his counterpart, the CIA man who was in charge of the Hmong that were supposed to protect them. They all knew things were getting hot. There was artillery fire and mortars every day. The Air Commandos out of Udorn, Thailand struck enemy positions around the mountain day and night. The men had started arming themselves with M16's and grenades.

"They had fashioned cargo slings and webbing over the side of the cliff to a small ledge to use as shelter from attack. As night fell on March 10, it was business as usual. The technicians were using the radar to control airstrikes within 12 kilometers of their position.

"What they did not know was that about twenty Hmong sappers from the Pathet Lao were climbing the cliff and would soon be upon them. In the early morning hours of March 11, five technicians operated the radar and five more, including Etchberger went over the edge of the cliff on the slings to get some rest in a small grotto on the ledge. The Sappers reached the top of the mountain around 0300. They came over the side of the cliffs and infiltrated past the defenders. Seemingly familiar with the site, they began destroying the buildings with grenades.

"Hearing the noise, technicians ran out of the front door of the operations building into a barrage of small arms fire. Three were killed instantly including their commander The rest scrambled over the edge of the cliff on the slings. The enemy saw them and started throwing grenades at the grotto where the other five had been sleeping and killed two of them. Etchberger, with M16 in hand, started holding off the enemy and trying to help his wounded team. The CIA man on the mountaintop was a former Green Beret named Huey Marlow. He was down by the helipad command center when he saw the explosion that destroyed the TACAN. He began advancing on the summit with an automatic shotgun, a few grenades and several Hmong.

"His group engaged in hand to hand combat on the way to the mountaintop. Marlow arrived at the radar site and found an emplaced machine gun position. He killed the crew and rescued the FAC that had been hiding behind one of the radar buildings. The technicians who were hanging in slings over the cliff returned fire and forced the enemy back.

"Marlow was still under fire from the opposite direction. He and his Hmong and the FAC from Vientiane fought their way back to the helicopter landing area and the command post. The Ambassador in Vientiane had lost touch with the situation after 0300, and radio contact was not re-established until about 0500. He then ordered a complete evacuation at 0715, an hour ahead of schedule. The Air America choppers who had been on standby immediately tried to access the site.

"As they approached the summit, they drew heavy fire from the Sappers. Marlow, down at the helipad, saw this and assumed the radar site was in enemy hands. He called in A-1E Sandy's on the facilities. The strike forced at least one enemy soldier over the side of the cliff where the remaining Americans were defending their position. There was a firefight and the enemy was killed.

"Following the airstrike, the Air America helicopters were able to approach the ridgeline to try to evacuate the remaining Americans.

"Hearing the choppers coming in gave CMSgt. Etchberger the opportunity he needed. Most of his team were wounded . Etchberger, keeping the Sappers at bay with his M16, got his men up to the radar site and started loading them into the helicopters. Time after time he refused to be evacuated so he could help one of his men. The choppers went in repeatedly to evacuate the American technicians, the CIA officers and the FAC.

"Finally, all of the live Americans were loaded onto the Air America Huey helicopter and Etchberger got on board. As they were taking off, an enemy soldier came out of hiding and emptied his AK47 assault rifle. Cmsgt. Etchberger was mortally wounded and died on the way to the hospital in Udorn. The CIA was eventually able to account for or recover eight of the 11 Americans killed on Phou Pha Thi. Starting late in the morning of the 11th, air strikes were directed at the summit every day for a week.

"In the aftermath of the fall of Lima Site 85, Phou Pha Thi, Ambassador Sullivan sent a personal message to General Momyer. In that message he states, 'In hindsight, it seems to me we should have pulled all technicians out the morning of 10 March, even if this means losing the last few hours of the installations capability. What concerns me most is not the defensive action, but the disruption of the preplanned evacuation procedure. It is still not clear why technical personnel went over the cliff to a narrow ledge rather than down the trail to the chopper pad. CIA personnel subsequently went up same trail to installation, so we know the trail was traversable, even under artillery fire.

" 'It is also not clear to me how a small Vietnamese suicide squad got to the installation site, although it seems they must have scaled the cliff.' " Elder threw down his report and just looked at his friends. "Now we know why Colonel Aderholt did everything he could do to bypass the 7th Air Force. They were incompetent.

"They set up a clandestine, Special Operations mission in a neutral country having a civil war. They sent in men to run it that had no combat training, and gave control of the site to a civilian bureaucrat. Now I ask you, what could go wrong?"

"It looks like the CIA came to the same conclusion we did. The fall of Phou Pha Thi was not an Intel failure. It was a leadership failure. Pure and simple." "A toast gentlemen," said Jesse as he was standing up. He held out his coffee cup and the others held theirs. "They weren't trained as Air Commandos, but they served and died like Air Commandos." "Here, here!" chimed in all three men. "And to Cmsgt. Richard Etchberger, who just had his Air Force Cross upgraded to the Medal of Honor, Here, here!" resounded through the room. CMSgt. Taylor started folding up his copy of the report and Jesse got up and went over to the window. He was standing there looking outside and he turned to the others and said, "It's a fine day to die, Gentlemen." Elder and CMSgt. Taylor both looked up and said in harmony, "It sure is."

It was getting late and Jesse had to drive home, so they called it a day. "Next time you come, I might have a surprise for you, Jesse," said Taylor. "Oh yeah, what would that be?" he asked. "Well," said Taylor, "you know Tom that stays at the end of the hall? "Yeah," said Jesse. "Well, he knows one of your friends from the war." "Who? "asked Jesse. "Fred Sheffield" "Now, how would he know Fred?" asked Jesse, whose interest had been piqued.

CMSgt. Taylor had that grin on his face that meant he was up to something. "He was an Air Commando pilot for 25 years. When he retired he went to work for the CIA." Jesse had his things together and was saying his goodbyes and he turned at the door and said. "Tell Tom I'd be happy to talk about Fred." CMSgt. Taylor, still grinning, said, "I knew you would be."

With that Jesse went to his car to head home. The old man and CMSgt. Taylor started to get ready for supper. CMSgt. Taylor said, "When is he coming back?" The old man didn't even look up, he just said, "Thursday."

Cmsgt. Richard Etchberger

Photo by, USAF photo

CMSgt.Etchberger's'

Medal of Honor

Citation reads as follows

The president of the United States of America, authorized by act of Congress, March 3, 1863, has awarded, in the name of the Congress, the Medal of Honor to Chief Master Sgt. Richard L. Etchberger, United States Air Force, for conspicuous gallantry and intrepidity at the risk of life, above and beyond the call of duty.

Chief Master Sgt. Richard L. Etchberger distinguished himself by extraordinary heroism on March 11, 1968, in the country of Laos. While assigned as Ground Radar Superintendent, Detachment 1, 1043rd Radar Evacuation Squadron. On that day, Chief Etchberger and his team of technicians were manning a top-secret defensive position at Lima Site 85 when the base was overrun by an enemy ground force. Receiving sustained and withering heavy artillery attacks directly upon his unit's position, Chief Etchberger's entire crew lay dead or severely wounded.

Despite having received little or no combat training, Chief Etchberger single-handedly held off the enemy with an M-16, while simultaneously directing air strikes into the area and calling for air rescue.

Because of his fierce defense and heroic and selfless actions, he was able to deny the enemy access to his position and save the lives of his remaining crew. With the arrival of the rescue aircraft, Chief Etchberger without hesitation repeatedly and deliberately risked his own life, exposing himself to heavy enemy fire, in order to place three surviving wounded comrades into rescue slings hanging from the hovering helicopter waiting to airlift them to safety. With his remaining crew safely aboard, Chief Etchberger finally climbed into the evacuation sling himself, only to be fatally wounded by enemy ground fire as he was being raised into the aircraft. Chief Etchberger's bravery and determination in the face of persistent enemy fire and overwhelming odds are in keeping with the highest standards of performance and traditions of military service. Chief Etchberger's gallantry, self-sacrifice, and profound concern for his fellow men, at risk of his life, above and beyond the call of duty, reflect the

Martin

highest credit on himself and the United States Air
Force.

#6

of the

Sagas of the Air Commandos

There are Black Ops

and then there are

Missions that don't Exist

Ryan was making his way through the countryside, on his way to visit the old man. He came with his dad, Jesse , many times over the years and he enjoyed the visits. His dad could not come today because of his own medical appointments. Today may be the day that the old man would answer some questions for him about his dad. He knew about some things; his dad would always tell him how great the Air Commandos were and some of the things they did, but he never really got into what he had done. Today may be the day thought Ryan as he pulled into the nursing home parking lot. He had what he thought the old man needed, a pint of good whiskey and an ear for listening. As he approached the door to the nursing home, he hoped it would be enough.

Ryan walked into the nursing home lobby and passed by the aviary with the parakeets singing away and some old veterans sitting in wheelchairs listening and watching and waiting to die.

He knew his dad never wanted to live here. Someday Ryan would bring him home to live with him. He knew his dad would never become a burden; it was just not in him. Ryan checked in at the nurses' station the way his dad always did. Nurse Tricia was behind the desk. "How is the old Colonel today?" he asked. Nurse Tricia looked up with that winning smile and said, "same as usual. Where's your dad today?" "Oh, he had some appointments at the VA," Ryan answered. "Well, it's good to see you. Go on back and cheer him up" she replied. "Will do," Ryan said with a smile and a little wave. Ryan walked down the familiar hall until he came to the old man's room. He tapped on the door frame with his hand and said, "Knock, Knock" in a fairly loud voice so the Colonel could hear him. Elder looked up from a book he was reading and his eyes lit up. "Well, what a surprise, I did not think I would be getting any company today, and here you are." he smiled broadly. "How are those boys of yours?" "Growing like weeds," answered Ryan. The two men shook hands and Ryan gave him the whiskey. The old man, grinned and put the bottle away and rolled over to the counter to make a pot of coffee. As he made the coffee he turned to Ryan and said, "you always have a bunch of questions for me and your dad; what's it going to be today?" "Well, said Ryan, I always get a pretty good picture of what the Air Commandos did in Vietnam and Southeast Asia, but I never seem to hear about what you and my dad did. It always seems to be someone else. I would like to know some of the things my dad did in the war. He talks about Vietnam like it was a vacation.

"All fun and games. I know there is more to it than that, and I want to know about it." Elder looked at Ryan and then turned to finish making the coffee. He sat down while the coffee pot started and looked out of the window. "I am not sure I can tell you." said the old man.

"Why not?" asked Ryan. "Because," said the old man, who now seemed to be distressed. "It's not my place." Ryan sat looking at the old man and said, "You know he will never tell me, and I have boys that will want to know who their grandfather was." The old man winced and turned and looked out of the window. "If I tell you some things, you have to promise that you will never let him know I told you. And some of this is going to seem like it couldn't be true, but it is." Ryan looked at the old man and said "I want to know." The old man looked out of the window and finally said. "Alright, if that is what you want." Ryan looked steadily on and said. "It is."

"Well, it was late in the war when your father showed up. He was assigned to me as my loadmaster and he was a good one. I knew something was different about him from the start. It didn't seem to matter to him what the mission was, he was ready to do it."

Martin

"What do you mean, different? " Ryan asked.
"Well," said the old man, "for starters he shows up at the
squadron in Phan Rang a week early. Now you might not
know this but the Military is fairly strict on timetables. He
was not even supposed to be able to get into the country.
But it seems that his brother was in the Army and stationed
up at Hue, Phu Bai. He was scheduled to ship out and then
your dad would be able to come into the war zone. So, him
just being there could have gotten him and the commander
in real trouble. He just flies in one day on a C-123 from Cam
Ron Bay and marches into the commander's office,
introduces himself and asks for help finding his brother so
he could visit before his brother went home. Well, the
commander was pissed and proceeded to chew your dad up
one side and down other. He screamed at him for about
ten minutes and asked him if he had anything to say for
himself. From what I hear, your dad just sat there and
calmly said he needed to see his brother before he went
home because there was no guarantee he was going to
make it through his tour. The commander just looked at
him and then picked up the phone and told someone to
send in one of the young navigators. They just looked at
each other for about two minutes and this young guy, a first
lieutenant, came in.

"The commander told him to help your dad find his brother so he could see him before he left the country. He told your dad not to process one piece of paper showing that he was in country before his brother left. That was it. They found his brother processing out in Saigon, flew your dad down there on some phony orders and they got to spend the day together. Anyone else would have been court-martialed." Ryan was stunned. "I knew he had visited with my uncle, but I did not know it was so complicated." "Yep," said the old man. "Your dad risked his whole career on that move. Getting out of the Philippines was the hard part. But it was important to him. He came back, processed in Country, and we started flying together.

"One of the missions that we had was one that was kind of off the books. We had listening posts deep in North Vietnam. They were manned by Seal teams for 45 days or so at a time and then they were rotated out and a new team took over. We got the first one right after your daddy came. We called him Wayne then. I took the radio message and gathered the crew together and explained to them that we were going into North Vietnam and we would be on our own.

"There would be no top cap, no Sandy's for ground support and if we were compromised or shot down, the Air Force would not know who we were. I told him that if we were captured it would not be pretty. He just grinned at me, and then the crazy son of a buck pulled this bullet out of his flight suit sleeve pocket, and said, 'don't worry, I am not going to be captured. This is my magic bullet. It is for me if I run out of bullets before I run out of enemy.' He laughed, put the bullet back and said, 'let's go'. "Now they had about eight of those listening posts that I know of, and we would get this trip about once a month.

"We would get the call and go up to Da Nang and empty any cargo that we already had, and load up the Seal Team with their crypto boxes. There were usually about six of them, and back then Seals were pretty good to work with; it was before they made a reality TV show out of them. Your dad told me a couple of years ago that they must have greatly expanded the Seal Teams, and when I asked him why, he said, 'well everybody I meet that was in the navy was a seal and not only that, they were all on Seal Team Six.'" Both men stopped for a sip of coffee and a good laugh because that sounded exactly like something he would say. The old man continued, "we would load up and then take off for a point in North Vietnam."

"The reason they used us is because it was too far for a helicopter. We would get feet wet right out of Da Nang and fly north. We would be within sight of the coast and we could see the coast watchers in their fishing boats. I would make a big announcement.

"We are now in North Vietnam and they know we are coming. We would fly up the coast for a little while, until we got to our landmark. All of the drop-offs had landmarks to follow, as we had no navigation equipment on a C-123. On this day it was two mountains with a river coming out of the center into the South China Sea. When we got there, we turned left and flew into the interior. We would fly along and follow a list of landmarks until we got to where we would land and let this group off and pick up the ones that were there already. We always had to time it so that we would get there at dusk. We wanted to get in and land and have it dark when we took off. We knew that the North Vietnamese knew we were there, so, getting back out without getting shot up or having missiles fired at us was easier in the dark. Now, normally, we would fly in, do the drop off and the pick-up, and fly out and be back at Da Nang by Beer thirty. Sometimes, though, things didn't go as planned.

Martin

"Sometimes the VC would find the Seal team and wait in ambush for them to be picked up. When that happened, all hell would break loose. You couldn't drop off the new team because the location had been compromised and you had to extract the team that was there. The problem was, you really never knew what was going to happen until you landed. These landing strips were cut out of the jungle on the sides of mountains at extreme angles. About the only planes that could land there were our C123's, C7's and Air America's Porters. So here we are, at dusk, and we find the mountain and the airstrip. We come around and I bring it in for an assault landing and boom! We are there and we are down. We have been in contact with the team on the ground and all seems right with the world. Your dad opens the ramp and door in the back of the plane and all hell breaks loose. The team we had was starting to offload and the ground team was just clearing the tree line. The North Vietnamese opened up with everything they had.

"Now I was kind of busy because I had to turn the airplane around so we could take off. So, picture this, the air is full of tracers, we are under full attack, and the engines are screaming to move this plane on the dirt.

"I turn around to look into the back and there is your dad; he has a pistol in one hand and a flashlight in the other. He is directing the ground team to run for the airplane even though it is moving. He had already stationed the team we were bringing at the ramp and the doors provided cover and to help the ground team onto the airplane. I continued the turn around and when it was complete, I ran up the engines for the assault takeoff downhill. I looked back and saw your dad jumping into the aircraft, screaming on the headsets to GO, GO, GO. He had stayed on the ground, returning enemy fire, until the last man was on the aircraft. I barely had time to turn the aircraft around, I tell you. I have never seen anything like it. I completed the takeoff roll and we got airborne and soon after we were feet wet.

"We had twelve men and their equipment and the airplane was flying. I looked around and asked him if everything was OK and he just grinned and said that he hoped that wasn't all they had. I told him to be patient, I was sure that Charley had a little more. We flew back to Da Nang and dropped off the Seals and went about our business. That was one of the missions that did not exist.

Martin

"We could not let anyone know that we had people stationed in North Vietnam who listened to everything that was said on the radio." Ryan, listening intently to the story, asked, "How many of those missions ended up that way?" The old man thought about it and then said, "There were only two. All the rest went as planned. Now another type of mission that we had that was not on the books was when one of our Special Operations teams were operating where they were not supposed to be and got caught.

"We would send fighter support if we could and fly over and airdrop food and ammo and whatever else they needed. These missions would come out of the blue, because, we never knew where these guys were operating. We would just be flying along, doing whatever Saigon had for us that day, and then we would be diverted to the other mission. Most of the time it was a quick in and out. We would fly in and airdrop supplies of food and ammunition or whatever they needed and then just get out. I remember one time, though, that the powers that be in Saigon thought they were smarter than everyone else. There was a team that was operating deep inside enemy territory and had made contact with a vastly superior enemy force. We couldn't rescue them with helicopters because of where they were.

"It would have been hard to send fighters into deep jungle because they can't hit anything. We heard about this situation on the radio and were waiting for one of our birds to be diverted to go airdrop supplies to them.

"They were holding their own, but running low on food and ammo. We wait and wait until finally we hear that a C-130 from Guam is going to do it. Now, this is bad. A 130 has a lot of capabilities and airdrop is one of them, but they are big and they come pretty straight into a drop zone. It makes them a good target. I got on the radio to Saigon and told them a C-123 would be the best plane for this particular drop. They basically told me to mind my own business. About an hour later we heard on the radio that the C-130 was loaded and inbound. So, this C-130 crew was getting ready for a little combat action. Little did they know that the enemy was expecting a re-supply and had, not only small arms, but anti-aircraft guns. The C-130 made contact with the team on the ground and came around to line up for the drop. They got down to 750 ft. and slowed down. The enemy had quickly positioned its guns and as the aircraft approached, they let him have it.

"That plane was shot up so bad that it immediately broke off the drop run and limped away. It finally had to land in the grass at Phnom Penh.

Martin

"The gear was shot out and he landed with just two engines. Those boys were lucky to be able to tell about that one. Now we were expecting to get the call or one of our sister ships. This kind of drop is right up our alley. It didn't take long and we heard that they were diverting a C7 Caribou to make a drop attempt. Now we didn't understand this at all. This was the worst choice you could possibly make. The C7 was much smaller and slower than the C-123 and had less power. The crew talked about it and we thought that after this we might not make that drop. After all, the enemy would be sitting there, all set up, and waiting to blow you out of the sky. In less than an hour, the C7 was loaded and inbound. They went to the location and made their standard airdrop approach. The enemy shot them down. Literally blew them out of the sky. The plane went down and all hands were lost.

"We were listening to the radio chatter while this is going on in stunned silence. Those people in Saigon did not know what they were doing. The next person we heard on the radio was our squadron commander and he was trying to raise us. I answered him and he said that he had talked to the powers that be in Saigon and they had agreed that an Air Commando C-123 was the only choice and would we be willing to do it?

Martin

"He said he had told Saigon that it would be voluntary only after the previous debacle. I asked him to wait a minute and I asked the crew what they wanted to do. Out of the back of the airplane your dad came on the headset. 'Hell, yes we're going to do it. Those boys are going to die down there unless we do this.' The engineer, The Cinncinatti Kid we called him, said 'I agree, if we don't go, they don't have a chance.' I kind of smiled at the responses and looked over at the Co-pilot. He had just finished wrapping a white scarf around his neck and said, 'I can't believe we are still talking about this.'

"I got back on the radio and told our commander that we were his volunteers. We were then diverted to Vientiane, Laos to load up. We landed in Vientiane and I went over to the Air America operations center to get a flight plan and pick up a navigator. We had some there helping with setting up some radio beacons. I got this kid that looked about 15 but was a 25-year-old navigator. He had been working with Air America and was very good at Air drop.

"When we arrived at the plane, your dad and the engineer were tying down two airdrop bundles and rigging the chutes.

Martin

"I went back to inspect the load and wondered how a case of beer and two cartons of Winston cigarettes had gotten on one of the bundles. "What's this," I asked your dad. He looked up and said that it was the reason I owed him five dollars. While your dad, the loadmaster, had received the load and started rigging it, they had decided that the engineer would go to the BX and get supplies.

"The Air America boys were only too happy to help. I also noticed a pile of flak vests in the right-hand door well. Your dad had gotten them to lay on so that groundfire coming through the floor would not wound him. He had also rigged up some ropes over the frame members so that after the load was clear of the aircraft, he could close the ramp and the door without getting up. It was really smart, I tell you. So, here we are, an old pilot, a copilot that thinks he's in WWI, and an engineer and a loadmaster that think they are in the wild west. We picked up another loadmaster for the drop; it really does take two. The navigator thinks all of this is funny and says so. We just ignored him and buttoned everything up and took off into a late afternoon of who knows what. It took us a little over an hour to get to the drop zone. We knew that the enemy would be waiting for us.

Martin

"I flew over the drop zone at 10,000 ft. a couple of times and finally told the crew that I thought we could do it. They all agreed and we got down to 8,000 ft. and started the drop run. We knew that all approaches to the drop zone would be covered so we decided to go in high, put the nose over and dive on the target. I would pull up at the last minute and Jesse would drop the load. If the wings did not come off of the aircraft, we just might make it. So, here we are, coming in high and fast. When we get in range of the drop zone I push the nose over until we are looking straight at the ground. The engines are screaming and we have the jets fired up. Your dad, the loadmaster, has strapped himself to the airplane. Nobody says a word and I start pulling back on the yoke. It is incredibly hard. I look at the copilot and he pulls with me. The ground is starting to get closer very fast. The nose starts coming up and the navigator is looking out of the back of the airplane. As the plane becomes level, all hell breaks loose. We are getting hit from all sides.

"The navigator says, 'Green Light' and your dad released the load. He told me later that he could see pieces of the wooden pallets flying off after being hit by groundfire.

Martin

"I heard his voice on the intercom when he said 'Load Clear'. Now the plane had just become level and I knew that if I pulled up in a standard fashion, the enemy would chew us up. So, I kept the plane level, just above treetop level and firewalled the engines and brought the jets up to 100%. We actually hit the top of the trees. It seemed like a long time, but, the whole thing was over in a minute or two. I looked into the back and the ramp was closed and here was Jesse standing on the ramp emptying his pistol into the jungle. I asked him why he did that, and he just looked at me and said, 'Why not?' We got home that night after dark with a shot up airplane and a crew that now thought that they could do anything. It was a great feeling." Ryan looked at the old man and asked, "Is that what changed him?" "What do you mean?" asked the old man. "Well, I know what he was when he got there, and I know what he is now." What changed him?" The old man looked away out of the window and then rubbed his chin with his hand. He was in distress and it was obvious. Ryan looked at the old man and said, "I really want to know, and you are the only one who can tell me." "Well", said the old man, "you may be right, but I am not sure I know." "What do you mean?" Ryan asked. "Well, you see, there was a time when your dad flew for someone else," said Elder.

"You mean Southern Air Transport and Central America; I knew about that," said Ryan. "No," said the old man. "While we were in Vietnam, I went home for R&R and your dad was sheep dipped." "You got me on that one," said Ryan. "what does sheep dipped mean? It doesn't sound good." "You have to promise me on all that is sacred, that you will never let him know that I told you, or that you even know," said Elder. Ryan promised. Elder sat back in his chair and started talking. "I went on R&R and was going to be gone for two weeks . Your dad could have just flown with other pilots and crews until I got back, but he decided to take the offer of one of the spooks, the CIA guys that we were always running into and working with. The offer was that you would be discharged from the Air Force and become a civilian contractor for Air America, which was the CIA owned airlines. Then when you come back, you would be re-enlisted in the Air Force as if nothing had happened. I actually had cautioned against it, but your dad really wanted to see that side of the war. So off I went to R&R and off your dad went to see the war from a civilian point of view. I had a great time and when I returned, he was different.

Martin

"I understand there was an aircraft crash involved, and a short run through the jungle, but he never would tell me what happened while I was gone. But that is when he started saying, 'It's a good day to die' every morning. And that is when the really heavy drinking started.

"He would drink every night. I asked him about it, but he would be on the flight line on time every morning and would work all day. Maybe I should have had a talk with the commander about it, but he seemed to be okay during the day." Ryan just sat there and asked, "so you really don't know what happened to him?" "No," said the old man. "Is there any way to verify any of this?" asked Ryan. The old man looked kind of miffed and said, "No, and I don't want you trying. If it makes you feel any better, when he dies, look at his military records. If you find a discharge and enlistment in Vietnam you will know this is true." Ryan mulled this information over for a while. He was sitting there in deep thought and the old man was pouring whiskey and coffees. Ryan looked over at Elder and asked, "Did you know a guy by the name of Fred Sheffield?" The old man nearly dropped his coffee cup. "How do you know about Fred?" Ryan was a little rattled at the response and said, "He and Dad are best friends."

Martin

Now the old man was surprised. "Really, how
long?" Ryan kind of thought about it for a minute and said,
"Since they ran into each other in about 1985." The old man
scratched his head and said, "You know, he never
mentioned that to me." Ryan said, "they told me they met
in Vietnam but not much else; do you know how they met?"
"Yeah, I do," said the old man, "it was strange. We were
out flying the line and had landed at some God forsaken
little dirt strip to re-supply our Vietnamese friends, and your
dad was in the back getting the pallets off of the airplane
and this guy shows up. We did not even see where he came
from, it was like he just appeared at the airplane. He was
ragged, dirty, his uniform was hanging off of him in tatters
and he had a full beard. Strangest looking fellow you ever
saw. Well, I was keeping an eye on him and he was talking
to your dad and he showed him some papers and the next
thing I know he is getting on the airplane and taking a seat.
So, I went on back to ask your dad what was going on.

"He told me that the guy was a special operations
guy from the Rangers and we were going to give him a ride
to Bien Hoa. I looked at your dad and asked him if the guy
had any orders. Your dad said yeah, he had orders that
would let him fly on anything available. Not only that, he
was flying as a crew member.

Martin

"Well, I had to see these orders, so I turned around and there he was holding out the orders; he was like some jungle wraith or something. I looked at him and said, 'You know I am going to call this in and verify it.' He looked at me and had this disconcerting grin and said, 'Sure, be my guest', and then he pointed to a number in the corner of the orders and told me to just give them that number. Well, we took off and in flight I called Saigon and verified those orders. I was talking to a two-star general before I knew it and he told me, in no uncertain terms, that I was to give this person all the support that I could. He was an outlier. He would go into enemy held territory and take out Viet Cong leadership.

"No insertions, no extractions; he walked in and he walked out. All anybody really knew for sure was that Viet Cong activity greatly decreased wherever he went." The old man finished his coffee and turned to Ryan and continued. "When we got to Bien Hoa, your dad and Fred were talking and laughing like they had known each other all their lives. Fred got off the plane and I gave him his orders back and told him it was a pleasure meeting him. Do you know what he told me? He told me that maybe next time he would teach me how to fly this plane.

"I was so mad I could spit. I turned around and yelled for your dad to come around there so he could get rid of this punk. Your dad came around the airplane and I turned around to dress down this insolent bastard and he was gone. I was standing there stuttering, I was so mad, and he was gone. I asked your dad where he had gone and he just shrugged his shoulders and went back to work.

"After we took off, I asked your dad what that guy was going to do in Bien Hoa. Jesse said, 'He said he was going to re-supply, his orders also said that he could carry unconventional weapons.' Well, I thought at least we are rid of him. And I thought we were." The old man was really getting wired up at the thought of Fred Sheffield. "We went about our business for the next week and we pulled back into Bien Hoa. I had forgotten all about our little visitor and I went into operations to file my flight plan. While I was gone this Fred guy goes and talks to your dad and is on the airplane when I get back. 'Where do you think you're going?' I asked. Fred looks up and just said, 'Victor 43'. I look right at him and told him, 'we aren't going to Victor 43.' Fred just grinned and said, 'then I'll go wherever you go.'

Martin

"I remembered talking to that two-star general, so I just muttered 'OK' and went to the cockpit. Right before I turned on the runway to takeoff, the tower called. I'll be darned if we weren't diverted to Victor 43. I just gritted my teeth and went on. Turns out this Fred fellow took a liking to your dad. We became his in-country taxi service. He would show up anytime and we would take him wherever he wanted to go. I thought he was done when he got shot up in New Orleans. He was a federal agent then." "No," said Ryan. "He moved to Mississippi and has a good business there. He and my dad have always been close. They helped each other in their business ventures over the years. And I remember one time when I was still in high school, our clothes dryer went on the fritz. You know Dad, he tried to fix it, but it looked like it was on its last legs. Then one morning, my mother got up to go to work and went into the kitchen and there was a new dryer sitting in the kitchen on a moving dolly. Well, mom came back to the bedroom where dad was getting dressed and told him there was a dryer in the kitchen. Dad pulled on his shirt and went to the kitchen and there it was.

"Mom was all upset asking where did it come from. Dad just grinned and told her Fred must have brought it.

"She wanted to know when, and he told her that it was probably about four in the morning, and she wanted to know how. Dad just shook his head and grinned, 'Honey,' he said, 'we may never know that.' He and Fred used to go out of town on business and they were supposed to be in Little Rock, but who knows?" The old man just listened and then he told Ryan, "You know this Fred guy, and there was a guy out west named Tim; the problem was, when they got together, they would do anything. It was kind of scary really." "They did stuff with you didn't they?" asked Ryan. Elder said, "Yes, they did, but we are not going to go there." "Well, Ok, but can you explain how he came to be called Jesse?" asked Ryan. The old man looked out of his window and asked for another cup of coffee. Ryan went over to the counter and poured a cup and then poured some whiskey in it. "You don't have to tell me if you don't want to," he said.

"I have already told you too much, so, I am going to tell you how he became Jesse and then we are done for the day, fair enough?" said Elder. "Fair enough." said Ryan.

"That nickname came about in two instances. Both of which I am surprised didn't put your dad and me in jail. On the first one, we were on a passenger run and were sitting at Vung Tau loading passengers."

Martin

"Your dad had given the passenger briefing and was strapping down the bags on the ramp. One guy is in the Army and has some beef with Air Force guys. You know, we live in better conditions and have better food than the grunts. It was always something. He was running his mouth and your dad handled it the way he always did. He told the guy if he wanted to ride, he would have to shut up. Well, this enraged the grunt and he started swinging a cane around. I came up to see what was happening and I was looking at your dad and the guy raised the cane to hit me. Your dad drew his service revolver and threatened to shoot the guy. I grabbed the cane and of course the grunt started screaming. The Security Police came up and I told them what had happened. They just grinned and told me they knew this guy and they would take care of it. I turned around and there was your dad just finishing up loading the passengers like nothing ever happened. So, I called out, 'You ready to go Jesse James?' He just grinned and gave me a thumbs up." Ryan was listening attentively and asked, "So, he was Jesse after that?" "Kind of," said the old man. "We called him that sometimes, but he was still Wayne some of the time." "But what made it stick?" asked Ryan. "Well," said the old man. "It was a most peculiar situation.

Martin

"We landed at Bien Hoa to pick up a load of mortar shells to take to a Special Forces camp. We landed and pulled the plane into a revetment. I walked into operations to file a flight plan and to talk to a couple of old buddies. Meanwhile, they had brought out pallets of mortar rounds and started loading the plane.

"They had three pallets on the plane when your dad noticed that the first pallet had been tampered with. He called the freight guy and showed him. They agreed that the pallet had to be removed. So, you dad told them to unload the plane and bring another pallet out. Now that was exactly the right thing to do and if I had been there it's what I would have done. But there is this First Lt. Ramp agent who came up to the plane and asked what was going on. Now, I did not know until later that your dad knew this guy and that they did not get along. He instantly starts yelling to the freight guys that he was going to fix the pallet and that we would not be unloading it. Your dad and the freight guys tried to explain that the pallet could be booby trapped and no one could touch it. The officer argued with the freight guys and finally just said, 'I will fix this.' He turned around and there stood Jesse blocking his way to the pallet. Your dad said, 'I can't let you do that sir.'

"The officer was irate by now and started yelling at your dad and trying to push his way to the pallet. That is when it happened. Your dad drew his service revolver and stuck it in the officer's face. He then told him in no uncertain terms that he would shoot him if he tried to touch the pallet. 'Now,' said your dad, 'back out of the airplane.' Now, I am in operations visiting with old friends, one of which is the commander of the Air Freight Squadron. Schedules being what they are, my buddy who is a bird colonel, decides to walk me back to the plane. We are walking down between the revetments when he stops and says, 'What the hell is going on there?' I look down toward the plane and here is your dad, my loadmaster, marching an officer down the ramp with a pistol in his face. Well, God knows what is going on. The colonel and I continue walking and I told him to be calm. We walked up to the group and I casually asked your dad why he was holding an Air Freight Officer at gunpoint.

"He started to tell me and the officer started yelling at him. The colonel told the officer to shut up and that he would get his turn, but he really wanted to hear this. So, your dad never moved. He stood perfectly still with the gun pointed at this officer's head and he told the story of what had gone on.

"The colonel turned to a SSgt. Air Freight guy and asked him for his side of the story. He said the exact same thing as your dad. The officer started with some histrionics and the colonel told him to be quiet. The colonel looked at me and asked me if I could control my loadmaster and I told him yes. He then said that what he really wanted to do was to tell your dad to shoot the guy. 'I have had trouble with him before, have your man stand down.' 'Yes sir,' I say, and I turned to your dad and said, 'stand down Jesse' and your dad holstered his weapon and went back to work. The colonel told the officer to go to his quarters and remain there until called. The freight guy replaced the pallet and we were ready to go.

"My buddy asked me what my loadmaster's name was and I told him, 'Jesse James'. We called him Jesse all the time after that. Anytime we needed an alias he used Jesse. It just seemed to fit." Ryan looked at the old man and said. "Thank you so much, what you have told me today explains a lot." Elder finished his coffee and said. "Explains a lot or explains nothing, you be the judge. Your Dad was the luckiest person I knew. When he walked away from threatening one guy with a pistol and holding an officer at gunpoint without even an inquiry, I knew he was special. The incident with the kid proves it."

Martin

"What incident?" Ryan asked. The old man sat back and said, "Well, one of our missions was to take fuel to outlying Army posts. They load a big bladder into the plane and fill it with fuel. Then we take the fuel to these little posts and they would pump the fuel into bladders they had in dugout pits beside the little runway. Now this operation caused quite a stir with the locals because the airplane was running the entire time.

"So, while the Army guys are pumping the fuel, your dad basically made sure that all was going well and he got into the habit of bringing and giving out candy to the children. This particular time, he had a group of children a little way from the plane. He looked over and saw what he thought was a live Claymore Mine. He immediately went to one of the Army guys and told him to get someone from ordnance disposal to come and get it. Now I had come to the back of the plane about the time your dad had told the guy to go get help. When he was done, he turned and saw one of the little boys going for the mine. Your dad ran toward the kid and just as the kid looked like he was triggering the mine he stopped and turned around. I was pulling my revolver to shoot the kid when he held up his hand and bowed his head. He truly thought that he was going to die right then.

Martin

"When nothing happened in a few seconds we all turned and looked at the kid. The mine was a dud. It had the back removed. One of the Army guys came and got it. Your dad walked back to the plane and I asked him if he was OK. He just looked at me and said, 'I will never kill a child.' Then he went back to work like nothing ever happened. All of these things affected him, had to." Ryan sat still for a little bit and the shook the old man's hand and thanked him for the insight.

Ryan tidied up a bit and then bid the old man farewell. The old man told him, "goodbye and bring those boys with you next time." They both were smiling and Ryan started for home, thinking about his dad.

#7

of the

Sagas of the Air Commandos

"I will do everything I can to help you"

The Story of the FAC's

Elder looked out over the wooded hillside and thought to himself that it would be nice to take a walk in the woods. It would never happen. The old man was too far gone to do that. He was confined to his wheelchair and that was never going to change. He was 94. He turned and looked at the clock on the wall, it was relentlessly ticking away the hours. How much longer did he have on this earth? He looked at his approaching death as a transition, something to look forward to, not something to fear. He was kind of looking forward to the day, but, until then he wanted to live a life with dignity. Jesse, the old man's loadmaster from the Vietnam War was his only friend, and he came and visited twice a week. Sometimes he brought his children and grandchildren with him. He was the closest thing to family that the old man had. He would be here soon. There were stories to tell and whiskey to drink. Life goes on, right up to the time it doesn't. "How are you doing Colonel?" Those were the words the old man had been waiting to hear. He turned and there was Jesse standing in the doorway. "Never better, how are you this fine day?" he said. "Pretty good. I had a nice smooth drive over and Ryan cleaned my boat for me," answered Jesse. "Well, that is good," said the old man as he turned in his wheelchair to make a pot of coffee.

"Ryan was asking me if you had ever flown FAC," Jesse said. The old man stopped what he was doing and half turned as he asked. "What made him ask that?" Jesse sat down in the old man's rocking chair and said. "Aww you know, looking at stuff on the internet. I told him I'd ask you, but I never heard you say anything about it." "Well now, that is true," said the old man. "I never did fly them, but they were always there, especially after an aircraft went down. They could stay in the air over a target for hours it seemed. Some of those pilots were real cowboys. A lot of them had been flying fighters before, but they took to the little planes like a duck to water."

Jesse looked over to the old man and asked, "They were special operations weren't they? They always seemed to be around our other aircraft." "Oh yes," said the old man. "They were all trained at Hurlbert Field. They were Air Commandos alright." "It seems like it would be boring, just sitting up there on the side and directing fire," said Jesse. "Well, it would be, if that is all you were doing. But they always seemed to show their true colors when the going got tough for others. They seemed to always do more." "What do you mean, more?" Jesse asked. "Well," said the old man. "let's start at the beginning.

Martin

"There were three types of aircraft that were used for Forward Air Control. You had the two place, single engine Cessna L-19, that we called a Bird Dog. It was flown by one pilot usually. Then you had the 02 Skymaster. It had one standard prop and a pusher prop in the back, a good airplane. Then you had the hot rod of the controllers, the OV-10 Bronco with twin turbo prop engines, a small two-man cockpit, and a twin boom tail. It could carry a centerline fuel tank and machine guns. Like I said, it was the hot rod of the group. Now, you can talk about small airplanes all day and what their mission was but it was the individual pilots that made the planes notable." The old man broke off the commentary and went to the counter to get a cup of coffee. Jesse got up and joined him. They poured the coffee and then, as if by magic, a pint bottle of whiskey appeared and they spiked the coffee. They took the cups back to their original positions. "Now, you take the Cessna; the Bird Dog came into service in 1947. It was an old airplane but it was stable in its simplicity. It was easy to fly and could be maintained in the field. Some of these planes were flown out of dirt strips in the middle of nowhere. I met one maintainer who said he hadn't worn a shirt in 7 months. Best tan I ever saw.

"You did not need a big hanger and special tools to keep it flying. All of the services had them, but in the Air Force they were flown by one pilot. He would get in there with his survival vest and an M-16 and ammo and go to work. It was not glamorous flying, but, the pilots that I talked to said it was fun flying." The old man paused and took a long sip of his coffee. "If you really want to know about the Bird Dog, you have to know about an Air Force Captain named Hilliard Almond Wilbanks, the greatest O1 pilot that ever flew the type. He was a great pilot, a great Air Commando, and a great human being." "Wow," said Jesse. "I think I have heard stories about him. Wasn't he the guy that attacked the enemy with smoke rockets?" "Yes he was," replied the old man. "You see, he was one of those guys that couldn't get enough of it. He felt he was saving lives every time he flew. Where a normal pilot in country in the same amount of time would have flown 250 missions, Wilbanks was on 488. On his last mission, he had been up directing artillery fire from naval ships offshore. After that, instead of going home, he went over to check out some Vietnamese Rangers who were on an operation.

"While he is there, he notices that there is a large concentration of NVA troops getting ready to ambush the Rangers.

"Now Wilbanks sees what is going on and gets on the radio with the Rangers. They are in a point position and for now there are no reinforcements. So, he calls in three Army helicopter gunships that are in the area. They come in and he directs their fire. On about the third run, one of the gunships gets hit really bad. Wilbanks in the Bird Dog sends the choppers back to escort the wounded one. Now, you might ask why send all three back when only one of them is hit. It is very simple, really. If the one that has been hit has to go down, one of the escorts will have to land and pick up the crew. The other one will have to patrol the area to keep the enemy from getting to them." Jesse just nodded and said, "That makes all the sense in the world." "So now," said the old man, "It is the Rangers against a much larger enemy force. Wilbanks is flying back and forth. He can see these enemy machine gun positions. The Rangers on the ground cannot.

"He uses up all of his smoke rockets keeping the enemy's heads down. You see, the enemy knows how this works. The FAC comes in and marks a position with smoke and then the fast movers, the fighters, come in and bomb and strafe the crap out of them.

Martin

"So, when Captain Wilbanks comes in and marks their position with a smoke rocket, they think they are about ready to get bombed so they hunker down in their holes and wait. It took a while but Wilbanks finally ran out of smoke rockets. He had a couple of smoke grenades with him and he made some passes and dropped those. But they ran out eventually, too. Captain Wilbanks was still giving the Rangers on the ground all the information that he had and he stayed with them. When the enemy started to move up the gun emplacements, Capt. Wilbanks knew he had to do something. So, what he did will go down in Air Commando history as one of the most heroic things we have ever done.

"He pulled out his M-16, stuck it out of the window and started making gun runs. The helicopter gunships would return, a flight of F-4's was on the way, but they would be no help for the Rangers. The North Vietnamese had left their positions with fixed bayonets. He flew over the enemy and fired directly on to their gun emplacements. It was awesome. For a while, the enemy was off balance and confused, but not for long. Wilbanks continued his assault. On the third run, inevitably, he was hit. He was lucky to do it as long as he did. They finally just shot him out of the air.

"An American on the ground said he was so low that they could hear the plane taking hits. The two gunship helicopters returned and engaged the enemy. The flight of F-4's arrived and turned the tide of battle. The gunships searched for the FAC. They found the plane, what was left of it, and recovered Hilliard Wilbanks, He died on the way to the hospital. They gave him the Medal of Honor for that. He deserved every bit of it.

"That is an amazing story," said Jesse. "Why did we call these guys Ravens?" "Well," said the old man, "that is a different story. You have to go back to the beginning. Back before the buildup. We were using our Combat Controllers for FAC's. They would either go up as a spotter with a pilot or, sometimes, they would fly the 01 themselves. Those were the guys called Ravens. Then, after the buildup, the powers that be in Saigon decided that all FAC's had to have rated pilots. So, they set up a school for them at Hurlburt and started pumping out FAC's. Now, that was all well and good, except that we had two wars going on. The one in Vietnam and the one in Laos. Now the generals in Saigon did not like the fact that there was a war going on, one country over, that they did not control. They tried their darndest, but the Air Commandos had friends in high places.

"One call to Curtis Lemay and some general got their butt chewed. That is the reason you can wear that bush hat you're so fond of. It will be forever part of our uniform, thanks to Curtis Lemay.

"Well, you and I are very familiar with the war in Laos," said Jesse. "That we are," said Elder, "but do you remember what our FAC's looked like? In Vietnam our boys had to toe the line. You've seen pictures of them wearing their flight suits and their flight helmets. While over in Laos, actually flying out of Thailand, they flew in blue jeans and T-shirts. It was more likely to see a cowboy hat than a flight helmet." Jesse held up a finger and the old man stopped. "Those were the guys up at Long Tieng, right?" The old man smiled and continued. "Yes, we were there many times. Our Air America friends were there, Ravens were there, and the Air Commandos ran operations out of there. It was the epitome of secret, jungle warfare. Those guys would fly over Laos doing interdiction on the Ho Chi Minh trail. It was dangerous work. No one wanted to get shot down or go down for any reason over Laos. Pilots that did disappeared. No POW camp, they just disappeared. You see, we were running a counter insurgency in Laos. We had teams in deep penetration to monitor the trail and try to convert people to our way of thinking."

"The Communists, the Pathet Lao and the Vietnamese did not like that at all. If it weren't for us and Air America they would have owned everything outright." "So, the Bird Dog was a good plane?" asked Jesse. "They were all good planes; it was the pilots that made them special," said the old man. "The planes themselves were just tools, like ours were. Just tools. The pilots liked the Bird Dog because they could see out of both sides of the aircraft and weren't restricted to left hand turns to see something. Any movement the enemy could anticipate was a death knell. Yep, those guys were great pilots and great Americans. People say that Wilbanks knowingly gave his life to protect those Vietnamese Rangers, and he is not the only one." "Another Bird Dog pilot did that too?" asked Jesse. "No, not a Bird Dog, a Bronco." The old man seemed deep in thought.

"Now that was the hot rod of the Vietnam War. Two 660 hp turbo prop engines and a two-place cockpit, one behind the other. Most of the time the Air Force just used one pilot, but, sometimes, like on night missions or Laotian missions a spotter or a translator went along in the back seat. The OV-10 Bronco also had guns. It had guns and rocket pods and an extended range centerline fuel tank.

Martin

"The Air Force, the Navy, and the Marine Corps
operated OV-10's. Some of the OV-10's had laser
designators. If you shot at one of those, he would go into a
flat left hand turn around the target and an F-4 would drop
a laser guided bomb and make them disappear. Sometimes
a Bronco would get shot at and go into a left hand turn just
to scare the enemy when they had no support coming. As I
understand it, we lost some Bronco's that way. The
Marines and the Navy always flew their OV-10's with guns.
That would be four M-60 machine guns under the wings in
pods. The Air Force, on the other hand, was on again, off
again.

"There was something called unnecessary heroics; I
never did figure out what that meant, but if they
determined we had damaged or lost a plane to that, then
they would take the guns off. That was stupid. Yes, the
plane was a tool, but, just as in carpentry, you want your
tools to be sharp. Just like Wilbanks in his Bird Dog, there
was a Bronco pilot that went down in history as a great man
and a great Air Commando. His name was Steven Bennett.
He was a Captain flying OV-10's out of the 20th TASS. He
was flying with a Marine Corps observer in the back seat.
His mission that day, was to direct and correct some Naval
artillery from offshore.

"The mission was uneventful and they were about ready to head home, when he heard on the radio that a friendly unit had made contact with a much larger enemy force. So, Captain Bennett and his observer went over to that area to check on the unit. When they arrived, it was obvious, that a much larger enemy force was attacking the friendlies.

"Bennett and another OV-10 circled while Bennett asked for Tactical Air Support. He was told there was none available. He then asked for artillery support from the ships offshore. His request was denied because the friendlies were too close and would get hit. They then decided that the other aircraft would stay up and observe enemy movements and Captain Bennett would go down and attack the enemy. He would do this by strafing them with machine guns and firing rockets at them. Now, some will ask, why fire smoke rockets at the enemy, and the answer is that they were not all smoke rockets. If you saw a FAC fire a rocket and it puffed white when it left the aircraft, it was a white phosphorus marker rocket. If, on the other hand, it puffed red, then it was full of flechettes. You remember those, nails with fins?" "Yes, of course," said Jesse. "Simple but effective. I have seen after action reports of people literally being nailed to trees."

"That's right," said the old man. "Nasty, but does a great job at keeping a large group of heads down. So, Captain Bennett and his observer start making gun runs and rocket runs on the enemy. They are doing a good job until the fifth run. They make the fifth run and as they are pulling out, they are hit by a newly introduced weapon, the Strella 7, a shoulder fired anti-aircraft missile. Now, this weapon was unknown at the time, and I am sure that if Captain Bennett had known about it, he would have taken a different tact. The Strella is a heat seeker, so it came in behind the aircraft and hit the left engine and blew the landing gear out of its pod. Captain Bennett flew the crippled aircraft away from the enemy and told his observer that they would have to bail out. The Bronco came with ejection seats and integral parachutes. His observer then told him that he could not bail out because the ejection seat had sustained damage and the parachute was shredded."

"Now, Bennett had a choice to make, he could bail out of the aircraft and leave the observer to try to crash land the aircraft, or he could try to land and give the observer a chance to survive. He decided that he would nurse the wounded plane out over the South China Sea and ditch the aircraft.

"As a man and as an Air Commando he really had no choice. He knew that no one had ever survived ditching a Bronco. It was the only choice he had. He got out over the water and the other Bronco stayed with him until he ditched it. It did not go well. The landing gear that had sustained the damage and was hanging down caught the water first and flipped the aircraft. With great difficulty, the observer extricated himself from the wreckage, but, was not able to get Captain Bennett out. The observer was rescued shortly thereafter and Captain Bennett's body was recovered the next day. Bennett gave his own life to save the life of the observer. I've said it once, and I will say it again. He was a great man, and a great Air Commando." The old man just sat quietly for a while. Jesse got up to refill the coffee cups without saying anything. They both had been in positions that could have taken their lives to save another. It changes a man. Captain Steven L. Bennett was awarded the Medal of Honor for his great sacrifice. That is why Air Commandos respect one another and everyone else is a lesser man. Jesse and the old man just sat for a while, thinking. They both had situations that had called for sacrifice; neither had failed to answer the call. The fact that those situations did not claim their lives did not diminish their importance to them.

Jesse broke the silence first. "So, we have Bird Dogs and OV-10's. What about 02's?" Elder thought about it and said, "well, the 02 was a good airplane, and had some good pilots. They did a great job, but I think the funniest thing I heard was how the Air Force got them in the first place. I read a story by Colonel Richard H. Wood (Ret.) about how they got them and how they got them to Vietnam.

"The Air Force needed a replacement for the 01 and for some reason they did not want to use OV-10's. So, they bought a bunch of Cessna Super Skymasters and called them 02's. They had a unique engine setup. The plane had a regular puller prop in the front and a pusher prop in the back with a duel tail boom. It was a Cessna, so reliability was not an issue. It was a good plane so the Air Force bought them. Now, these little planes were manufactured at the Cessna factory at Wichita Kansas. They were pumping them out at a pretty good clip, so the problem became how to get them to Vietnam? Air Force Systems Command was in charge of obtaining the aircraft which they did. Operating these aircraft was far beyond their purview. Now, there were three ways to get these planes from Kansas to the war zone in Southeast Asia. One, you fly them to the west coast and turn them over to the Army to ship by transport ship.

"Two, you take the wings off and transport two or three at a time by Air. Or three, you have pilots fly them over. This was a decision that Systems Command should never have made. The Air Force had a perfectly good organization called the 44th Aircraft Delivery Group. This group operated worldwide and managed the ferrying of all aircraft. Now you would think that the aircraft would be turned over to the 44th at the factory in Kansas. But no. Systems Command decided all on their own that they would deliver the planes to Vietnam. Since Systems Command had no pilots or experience in transporting aircraft, they contracted with a company in San Francisco to deliver the planes to Saigon. This company hired a bunch of pilots that could not find honest work. Now, this is a real winner. The planes were considered public aircraft because they belonged to the military as opposed to civil aircraft. That meant that the FAA did not require a pilot's license to fly them. No one is sure that all of the pilots had licenses. Some of them were pretty good and some of them were unqualified, scruffy-looking alcoholics."

No one told a story quite like the old man. He was getting wound up in this one. "The deal was cut and dried from the pilot's standpoint.

"When they were hired, they were given a ticket to Kansas. There they would get a quick checkout in an 02 and get ready for the trip of a lifetime. They would leave the factory in Kansas in groups of four. They would fly to Hamilton AFB on the west coast in California. They were supposed to monitor oil consumption, but, of course they did not. These guys were concentrating on staying in the air. Once at Hamilton, the Air Force, removed all the seats except the front left. The seats were shipped separately by air. Extra fuel tanks were installed and an extra oil tank. Top that off with a radio and the pilot had to use an emergency escape window on the side of the aircraft. These planes are now so overweight that if one engine goes the plane goes down. But keep in mind, these are brand new aircraft and they are Cessna's. They are as reliable as you can get.

"The route is Hamilton, to Hickam in Hawaii, that was the long leg. It should take the little planes about 13 hours; they had fuel for 14 ½ . Navigation was dead reckoning; there were no Nav aids in the planes. They took off from Hamilton in the general direction of Hawaii and hoped for the best. Now the round trip to Saigon and back was supposed to take a week and these guys were paid $800.

"They planned to make three trips a month. That is good money in 1967." "Yes it was," said Jesse. "But who is Colonel Wood and how did he figure into this little travesty?" "Well," said the old man, "If I remember right, he was the Safety Director at Hickam. At the time of the first group of 02's getting to Hawaii, he was attending a Coast Guard seminar on sea rescue. The 02's were lost and had sent out a Mayday. When that call came the Coast Guard ended the seminar and launched their C-130 and a couple of cutters to find the 02's.

"Find them they did; they herded them to the nearest runway which was Marine Corps Air Station at Kenehoe. Colonel Wood drove over the mountains to see what was going on, and there, he saw his first four 02's. They were soaked in oil because the pilots kept adding oil that the engines did not need, and they were out of gas. Literally, one of them ran out of gas taxiing in from the runway. It had taken over 14 hours, almost 15. The Coast Guard was threatening to send someone a bill for the rescue. It seemed that every flight of 02's got into some kind of trouble. Colonel Wood went to PACAF and headed the efforts to get this operation turned over to 44th. AFSC finally backed down and the 44th took over.

"The 44th wasn't too happy about these pilots that were on board, but they brought mission planning, weather analysis, and some organization to the party. The 02's were not allowed to fly unless a C-47 or a Caribou was with them. These planes could fly at their speed and provide the navigation.

"The delivery rate slowed down some, but most of the planes got there because of it. We only lost two planes. One was ditched due to engine failure on the Wake-Guam leg. The pilot managed to get out of the aircraft and was picked up by a Japanese cargo ship. The other went down in the Philippines killing the pilot. Colonel Wood was the Safety Officer so he checked out everything that happened. He told of one pilot who landed the plane nose first. He broke off the front gear and bent the prop. Smelling gin on the pilot, who told him the trim malfunctioned, Colonel Wood investigated. Seems the pilot was trying to trim the aircraft using the mic switch and he had actually bent the trim switch trying to talk to the tower. Case closed. The Colonel was lucky in one way. These planes would not be Air Force aircraft until they were delivered in Saigon. They weren't registered as civil aircraft so they could not have a civil accident. They were in regulatory limbo. Any accidents were non-events.

"Nobody cared and guess what? When it came time to bring these aircraft home, they took the wings off and flew them home on C-141s and C-130s. This is just another one of those stories that nobody is going to believe unless you were there and knew what the government is capable of." "That is for sure'" said Jesse. "You know, I talked to a couple of 02 pilots and they did not like it as much as the Bird Dog. It was hard to see out of the right side of the aircraft, so they tended to make left hand turns. Bad habit to be in. The enemy picked up on anything like that." "That is so true," said the old man. "Dexterity was a lifeline. It was jungle warfare. They could see you flying but it was hard for you to see them." The old man and Jesse James sat and enjoyed the last of their whiskey laced coffee. Jesse started to talk about the FAC's. "You know," he said, "those guys do not get the credit they deserve. They were in contact with the enemy almost every time they went up. They did everything, directing fire from the big ships offshore, directing fighters against enemy on the ground. They directed fire from American Fire bases. They also assisted in finding and communicating with downed airmen. They could loiter over a target for hours, making sure that guy on the ground knew he was not alone.

Martin

"Sometimes, over in Laos, they would troll the trail looking for trucks and troop movements. We lost a bunch of them. The planes they flew were cheap and we had a lot of them." The old man was looking out of the window in contemplation. "You know," he said, "I flew damn near everything the Air Force had except jets. I liked flying with a crew. Taking off in a small plane by yourself to make contact with the enemy and try to help fellow combatants on the ground just never appealed to me. I did some flying in them, but, I did not like it. We had other small planes, the Pilatus and the like. They weren't bad. Pilot, Co-Pilot and a loadmaster. It was a team. I liked that a lot better. That C-123K that we flew had pilot, co-pilot, engineer, loadmaster. We were a team. We left the base together in the morning and we came home together at night. We flew the same crew every day. We had relationships that meant something. I don't know about you, but that alone helped me a lot. I wasn't worried about what could happen to me. I was worried about all of you." "And we were worried about you," said Jesse. Elder looked at his friend, who once was the loadmaster on that team and said, "yes, and I am darned glad you did," a slight pause, "and still do.

"Have you ever heard anything from our engineer, Jim Springfield, what did you all call him?" "The Cincinatti Kid," Jesse said with a smile. "You could always depend on the Kid. He was on top of that plane, no matter what went wrong, and he would help me with the loads when it was needed. And, always remember, it was the Kid who saved those Red X's in the log book until we were in Bangkok. Our overnights in Thailand were always stretched to three days. And that was all the Kid."

"Oh, I remember," said the old man. "I remember very well." Jesse looked at his watch and the afternoon had gone. He started cleaning up the coffee cups and the old man hid the whiskey. Jesse straightened up on his way to the door and turned to the old man and said goodbye. The old man waved and said, "see you next time." As Jesse was almost out the door of the old man's room, he turned and said, "Hey Colonel, what's the first thing you say in the morning?" The old man winked and smiled as he said, "What a fine day to die." Jesse was smiling from the door and as he turned to leave, he said, "me too."

Martin

Photo by, USAF photo

The Medal of Honor Citation for

Hilliard A. Wilbanks

reads as follows

For conspicuous gallantry and intrepidity in action at the risk of his life above and beyond the call of duty. As a forward air controller Capt. Wilbanks was pilot of an unarmed, light aircraft flying visual reconnaissance ahead of a South Vietnam Army Ranger Battalion. His intensive search revealed a well-concealed and numerically superior hostile force poised to ambush the advancing rangers. The Viet Cong, realizing that Capt. Wilbanks' discovery had compromised their position and ability to launch a surprise attack, immediately fired on the small aircraft with all available firepower. The enemy then began advancing against the exposed forward elements of the ranger force which were pinned down by devastating fire. Capt. Wilbanks recognized that close support aircraft could not arrive in time to enable the rangers to withstand the advancing enemy onslaught. With full knowledge of the limitations of his unarmed, unarmored, light reconnaissance aircraft, and the great danger imposed by the enemy's vast firepower, he unhesitatingly assumed a covering, close support role. Flying through a hail of withering fire at treetop level, Capt. Wilbanks passed directly over the advancing enemy and inflicted many casualties by firing his rifle out of the side window of his aircraft. Despite increasingly intense antiaircraft fire, Capt. Wilbanks continued to completely disregard his own safety and made repeated low passes over the enemy to divert their fire away from the rangers. His daring tactics successfully interrupted the enemy advance, allowing the rangers to withdraw to safety from their perilous position. During his final courageous attack to protect the withdrawing forces, Capt. Wilbanks was mortally wounded and his bullet-riddled aircraft crashed between the opposing forces. Capt. Wilbanks' magnificent action saved numerous friendly personnel from certain injury or death. His unparalleled concern for his fellow man and his extraordinary heroism were in the highest traditions of the military service, and have reflected great credit upon himself and the U.S. Air Force.

Steven Bennett

Photo by, USAF photo

The Medal of Honor Citation for

Capt. Steven R. Bennett

Reads as follows

Capt. Bennett was the pilot of a light aircraft flying an artillery adjustment mission along a heavily defended segment of route structure. A large concentration of enemy troops was massing for an attack on a friendly unit. Capt. Bennett requested tactical air support but was advised that none was available. He also requested artillery support but this too was denied due to the close proximity of friendly troops to the target.

Capt. Bennett was determined to aid the endangered unit and elected to strafe the hostile positions. After four such passes, the enemy force began to retreat. Capt. Bennett continued the attack, but, as he completed his fifth strafing pass, his aircraft was struck by a surface-to-air missile, which severely damaged the left engine and the left main landing gear. As fire spread in the left engine, Capt. Bennett realized that recovery at a friendly airfield was impossible. He instructed his observer to prepare for an ejection, but was informed by the observer that his parachute had been shredded by the force of the impacting missile. Although Capt. Bennett had a good parachute, he knew that if he ejected, the observer would have no chance of survival. With complete disregard for his own life, Capt. Bennett elected to ditch the aircraft into the Gulf of Tonkin, even though he realized that a pilot of this type aircraft had never survived a ditching. The ensuing impact upon the water caused the aircraft to cartwheel and severely damaged the front cockpit, making escape for Capt. Bennett impossible. The observer successfully made his way out of the aircraft and was rescued. Capt. Bennett's unparalleled concern for his companion, extraordinary heroism and intrepidity above and beyond the call of duty, at the cost of his life, were in keeping with the highest traditions of the military service and reflect great credit upon himself and the U.S. Air Force.

#8

of the

Sagas of the Air Commandos

The Nimrods

Elder was smiling to himself. He was sitting in his wheelchair in front of his trunk of personal possessions. It was a large trunk and it contained mostly paperwork from a long and adventuresome life. There were orders and accommodations and photographs. The old man knew his friend Jesse would be in to see him today and he was just passing the time by sifting through old memories. He held in his hands two poems. He read them again and smiled. Those were the days, when men gathered to make war and, over a beer, write poetry. The first one was about flying those missions at night over the Ho Chi Minh trail in Laos.

ODE TO A NIMROD

The sleek black beauty sits on high

Frothing vengeance from the sky

A nimble candle lights a light,

The enemy convoy comes into sight.

The marks are placed, no more to say,

That valiant bird is on his prey.

With nerves of steel he makes each run

The guns are up but this is fun.

Martin

His load is gone, his guns are dry

The weary nimrod relieves a sigh.

Now the time has come and he must go

But God, he's been a fearless foe.

His wings are clipped, he'll cease to soar

The mighty hunter we'll be no more.

But in our hearts, they'll live again,

For we'll have known we've fought with men.

Anonymous

The second poem was about not making it home. The old

man kept the poem because he knew what it meant. He

had no fear of dying. He rather looked forward to it. It was

just getting transferred to a new assignment for him.

Martin

Fear Not Death

O peaceful sleep, what a wonderful adventure. No more

dreams of the past or dread of the future

to dream of beauty and rest at death

you have reached the crest.

To lie in peaceful harmony

To await no further agony

At last to meet those of which you have dreamed

The ones at night of which you have screamed.

Death not to fear

Just a final part of life, one to revere.

Not a chance of return

Nor would one for that to yearn

At last to be at rest of those of which you knew best.

Brothers and family of long ago,

When will life let us go.

No morbid thoughts do I reveal

Martin

for at times this is just how I feel.

We all will travel this way

for on this earth we cannot stay.

But to long for the feeling of relief

Is natural to some that suffer grief

Feel no pity for the writer of this verse

For within the days to come, remember,

it could have been worse.

Rather, look with fond remembrance of he that pass

and know that peace he has found at last.

Oh he will live from day to day

For a while on this earth he must stay.

Brothers of War, lives lost so long ago

Up to meet them he also must go.

With friendship and love

from God above.

The old man was still remembering the old days when the knock came from the door. "How's it going today, Colonel?" asked Jesse. "Never better," was the old man's stock answer. "Whatcha' got there?" asked Jesse. "Oh, just a couple of poems from the guys who flew the Nimrods out of NKP." Jesse held out his hand and the old man gave him the poems. Jesse took the time to read them. "Pretty good," Jesse said, as he put the papers down. "They are probably the least known group that flew over there. They probably did more damage to the enemy than all of the other groups put together." "Well, you might be right about that," said the old man. "They went up every night and hunted down and killed truck convoys on the Ho Chi Minh trail. The funny part was that they were so close to the trail. NKP was on the Laotian border of Thailand. NKP was a Royal Thai Air Base. So, when you took off and headed east, by the time you got to your altitude and finished your after-takeoff checklist, you were over the trail. We had scout teams looking for convoys and FAC's in the air. As soon as you got there it was time to go to work. They would make passes at the enemy until they were out of ordnance. The enemy had anti-aircraft guns and surface to air missiles. It was rough work, and they went up every night."

Jesse was looking at the poems and picked up
another set of papers asking, "What are these?" The old
man looked at them and said, "Those are a story Sgt. Taylor
printed off the internet. It's a good story about these two
guys who went to school together at Georgia Tech and went
into the Air Force. One became a pilot and one became a
navigator. They ended up flying together at NKP and one
night they got shot down. The crash was bad enough to
guarantee no survivors. Then a couple of years ago a joint
recovery team found the crash site and recovered remains
and artifacts of the two men. The remains were repatriated
and they were buried together at Arlington. It's a good
story.

"Why don't you make us a pot of coffee and I'll tell
you how we got a bunch of WWII bombers to Thailand."
Jesse grinned at his friend and went to the counter to make
the coffee. The old man pulled a pint bottle of whiskey
from its hiding place and the stage was set for a story. "You
see," started the old man, "back in WWII they had some
light attack type bomber aircraft. They had the A-20 Havoc
and the B-26 Marauder. In 1940 the Army put out the
requirement for a lightweight multi-role bomber for low
level precision bombing runs. Out of all the prototypes
submitted, they chose what we now know as the B-26.

Martin

"Now, they already had a B-26 in the Marauder, so they had to name this one the Invader and the A-26. It was the A-26 throughout WWII. After the war, when the B-26 Marauder had been taken out of service, they changed the name to the B-26 Invader. It was the B-26 Invader from then until Vietnam. It served in WWII, it dropped the first and last bombs in Korea, and served in Vietnam. It is the only bomber to serve in all three wars.

"It remained relatively unchanged until Vietnam." Jesse looked up from the coffeepot as it began to fill and asked, "were the Air Commando's the only ones operating them in Vietnam?" The old man thought for a minute and said. "Well, yes and no, The CIA had some of the WWII vintage planes but they were having problems with the wings falling off. Keep in mind, that this is an old airframe. The Commandos wanted them for night interdiction work on the Ho Chi Minh trail. So, we got a bunch of them from the boneyard at Davis Monthan AFB and sent them to On-Mark Engineering for modification. The wings were strengthened and the wing spars built up. The 2000 horsepower engines were replaced by Pratt and Whitney R2800's which were rated at 2500 horse power. They added permanent wingtip tanks for range.

Martin

"They imbedded three 50-caliber machine guns in each wing and added eight 50's in the nose. The modified B-26K was being sent to Thailand to operate over the trail at night. There was only one problem; because of diplomatic reasons, they could not base bombers in Thailand. To solve that problem, they changed the name back to A-26. It was OK to have an attack plane, but not a bomber. So, with its new name it was sent to Thailand and assumed its new call sign of Nimrod-- A biblical reference to the Great Hunter, Noah's grandson, I believe. The A-26's, or Nimrods were stationed at NKP, Nakhon Phanom Royal Thai Air Base. Now this place was right on the Mekong River which was the border with Laos. This was the home of the 56th Air Commando Wing. The Nimrods were the 606th Air Commando Squadron. There were other squadrons there too. There were A1-E's or Sandy's for close air support and rescue work, and UC-123's, OV-10's, and 0-2's for FAC work, and there were these little U-10's to fill the counter insurgency gaps. All in all, it was a pretty wild bunch. They were known as the Laotian Highway Patrol." "How many on the crew?" asked Jesse. The old man looked over at the coffee pot and back at Jesse. Seeing the gesture, he got up to pour two cups of coffee. "Two," the old man answered. "A pilot in the left seat and a navigator in the right seat.

"The cockpit had side by side seats and dual controls. The navigators could and did fly the aircraft. If a pilot got wounded the navigator could bring the ship home and land it. That is why I taught you to land a C-123." "Yeah, that's right, I always wondered though how I was going to get you out of the seat," said Jesse. The old man smiled as he poured a shot of whiskey into his coffee cup. "You know, some things just have to be figured out when they happen." Jesse held out his cup to get a shot and admired the old man. His memory was fantastic and he was the repository of information on three wars and countless conflicts. Jesse wondered what would happen when the old man finally died. "What exactly did the navigators do on a B-26?" asked Jesse. "Well," said the old man, "it wasn't exactly like any other aircraft. I mean you weren't going far and there wasn't any Nav gear.

"So the navigators operated the radios, they had certain responsibilities on the engine start checklist, and managed the fuel tanks by feeding, cross feeding' and balancing them. They monitored the engines and navigated by TACAN. The navigator would fly the aircraft to relieve the pilot and would arm the weapons systems.

Martin

"During a strike, he would call out altitudes and bank angles for the pilot." "I wonder why they just didn't use two pilots?" said Jesse. The old man rubbed his chin and said "you know, I wondered that myself, until I talked to some of the pilots that flew that mission. It was so specific to train for one job or the other. They couldn't afford to get someone trained for the right seat and have them get promoted to Aircraft Commander. You would have to start training someone new. It wasn't like they did trail interdiction one night and flares one night and then general cargo somewhere else. That's why those guys flew hard crews. They got used to each other, just like we did."

"That makes sense," said Jesse. "How bad were the losses?" The old man finished his coffee and held out the cup to get a refill. "Well, as far as I know they weren't that bad. The problem was that you were flying an old WWII propeller driven airplane, fully loaded with armament, at night, in the mountains of the most hostile airspace on the planet. If you were hit bad, you crashed, and in that environment, it was really hard to rescue someone.

"Sometimes you would read a report and it would say, crash landed no survivors, body not recovered. Everybody knew that you did not want to get shot down over Laos.

"On top of that, the B-26 did not have ejection seats. If you had to bail out, you would jettison the canopies and crawl out and dive over the wing. You would be between the props while you were climbing out. The numbers weren't bad, but any losses were terrible." "Yeah, I can see that," Jesse said, deep in thought. "So why did the 7th Air Force dislike the Air Commandos so much?"

"Well," said the old man, "The 7th Air Force was an administrative organization. It disliked everything it did not have direct control over. We belonged to the Eighth Air Force and they understood our mission. The Seventh in Saigon were more concerned about fighting a war with fast movers than the real mission. There was an entire Air Force over in Thailand that they had no control over and it chapped their butt every day. Of course, the fact that they were doing a job that was necessary and a job that the 7th couldn't do did not matter. I don't think, to this day, that the Senior Officers of the 7th Air Force understood the mission of the Air Commandos."

"The mission was unlike anything the Air Force had done since Korea. I was around for that, so I know. That group at NKP were trained by Ben King at Hurlbert Field. They were commanded by Heinie Aderholt. We called him Air Commando One. It was very much a 'damn the paperwork, full speed ahead' type of deal. The 7th also did not like the fact that so much of what we did was disavowed. Examples were civilian clothes, sanitized aircraft, and violating the sovereignty of neutral nations; you and I flew some of those insertions and extractions. It was up to the State Department to iron things out if we got caught. The 7th Air Force wanted to use fast mover fighter jets on interdiction runs in the jungle. It never worked, couldn't work. Aderholt, on the other hand, understood how a counterinsurgency worked. He wanted Commandos to fight communist aggression and that's what he built in Thailand. He was the one who got the Air Force to buy U-10 aircraft for COIN or 123's that you and I flew. He was behind the contract to rebuild 40 B-26 invaders. You remember what it looked like at NKP. Rows of B-26 Nimrods, T-28 Zorro's, O2 Skymasters, OV-10 Bronco's, A-1E Sandy's, C-123K Candlesticks, and A-37 Tweets. Nowhere else in the theater was there anything like this. And it was there to find and kill trucks, and to interdict the flow of "supplies from North Vietnam to South Vietnam. That one little unit in Thailand did more to stem the flow of supplies than the entire 7th Air Force."

The old man sat back and sipped his coffee. Jesse leaned back in his chair and asked, "what's going to happen to all of these stories when you die?" The old man wasn't the least bit taken aback by such a question. He looked at Jesse and said, "That's why I am telling you everything I know. I am 94 years old and my last flight can't be that far off. When I go, all this information will belong to you. Then it will be up to you to pass it along and let younger folks know how it started and what we did to begin Special Operations as they know it today. Basically, you will become the old man." He was smiling at the thought of passing on to a new mission. Jesse knew the old man's time was short; that is why he came so often. He wanted the information to pass to his son Ryan and to his boys. He smiled at the old man, and said, "OK, let's go over a full mission out of NKP." The old man replied, "OK, but let's start at the beginning."

The old man leaned back in his wheelchair and began. "We had planted sensors out on the trail that would give us information on movements of trucks or men.

Martin

"Now this was high tech at the time, but people would laugh at it now. The sensors were of different frequencies and they were dropped in different segments of the trail. So, when we got information from a sensor, we knew, in general, what area of the trail it was on. On top of the sensors, we had scout teams made up of Thai, Laotian, and Cambodian soldiers. Now it will never be known but we sent our Air Commandos with those teams to train them.

"They would identify a convoy and then track it hopefully to a truck park. We would gladly attack an individual convoy, but a truck park was like hitting the jackpot. The convoys would travel during the day and then park at night. The truck parks were big operations. They had fuel, food, overnight accommodations and medical services. Us killing a truck park was big time."

"We had O2s and OV-10s, UC-123 flare ships and FAC's and they were on the trail day and night. They were constantly looking for movement on the trail and for choke points to increase the battle damage inflicted upon our enemy. We did not fly as much in the daytime as the trail was full of anti-aircraft guns and if they could see you, they could kill you. Night, that was our time."

"We knew they were moving and so were we. The FAC's were the first ones on the trail at night looking for movement.

"The C-123 Candlesticks were there waiting for contact to light up the night. Then there was the Hammer, the B-26 Nimrods with bombs, napalm, and eight 50 Cal. machine guns in the nose and four more in the wings. The pilot and navigator would take off from NKP and fly over to their assigned section of the trail. Now keep in mind, this was mountainous terrain. There were these limestone columns that rose hundreds of feet called Karst, and there was traffic. That is what these guys flew into every night.

"The FAC would identify a target and mark it with rockets. The Candlesticks would fly over and drop these big white phosphorus parachute flares that would light up the night like day time. Now, we did not use flares all of the time. They would light up the Nimrods as they came in on the target and they would shoot at them with the anti-aircraft guns.

"The FAC's and the Nimrods were on the radio together and the Nimrods would roll in on the target. The pilot would call out the munitions to be dropped and the navigator would arm it and call out altitudes to the pilot as a lot of these runs could be described as dive bombing.

"The navigators would do everything a normal Co-pilot would do and act as a weapons officer too. So, once the Nimrod engaged it was busy.

"There were FAC's and Candlesticks to keep track of, there was anti-aircraft fire to keep track of, but, all in all, it was quite a show. Those eight 50's in the nose were great, but, every fifth round was a tracer. Tracers were good due to the fact that they told you exactly where your ammo was hitting. The downside is, that they told the enemy exactly where you were. The dark was the best defense a Nimrod had. The plane was blacked out with black paint, no lights, and no insignia to reflect light. On a normal night, once contact with the enemy had been made, the Nimrods would make pass after pass until they were out of ordnance. No one wanted to come home and land with bombs in the racks under the wings, so, on a slow night, the FAC's would find a choke point to expend excess ordnance. The FAC's tried to keep a record of battle damage because the Nimrod crews were really just too busy. After it was all over, they crews would fly back to NKP. They would usually get home about 4 o'clock in the morning. They would proceed to operations to debrief and do the paperwork. Being that a majority of their mission was at night, the clubs were open.

"The crews would gather and share information that they had gleaned from the mission. They would raise a little hell in the clubs. These men were Air Commandos, they had no tomorrow.

"They knew that tomorrow night, they would have to suit up and go out and do it again. Every mission was like cheating death. They deserved whatever fun they had." Silently, Jesse got up to refill the coffee cups and to make a fresh pot. He then turned to the old man and asked, "what about the Candlestick crews? I only flew candles twice on those black ops up in North Vietnam." "Well," started the old man, "the Candlestick crews did just what you did. They carried a navigator and they carried two loadmasters and sometimes a crew chief and other extra men. It was too rough to have the doors open so they made a wooden launch tube that fit between the ramp and the cargo door. Then either one of the loadmasters or a crew chief would sit on the door with the launch tube between his legs. The loadmaster would pull a flare from the rack and arm it. Then he would hand it to the man sitting on the cargo door. This man would slide the flare through the launch tube into the air. The altitude change would ignite the flare and night would turn into day.

Martin

"Then the loadmasters would usually sit on trash cans in front of the paratroop doors and call breaks when they saw enemy fire coming at them. Once again, this was rough flying. We were in an old airplane with no hydraulic assist. The pilot had to muscle this thing around mountainous terrain with the Karst for four hours or so.

"It was tough. Sometimes there would be fighters involved, coming back home with bombs left. They would come over the trail and the FAC's would try to bring them in on a target. They never did any good. They were too high because of the terrain and too fast to hit anything. Basically, they just clogged up the airspace with something else to look out for." The old man sighed and looked at the clock on the wall as if to say 'how long?'

"You know that the Candlesticks did not have a set mission that they did every night. Sometimes, if there was known traffic, they would support the Nimrods and so would the Zorro's. Sometimes though, there was no known traffic or someone else needed help. Colonel Aderholt was the one that got the C-123's to NKP to use as Candlesticks. Before that they were using C-130 Blindbat flare ships out of Ubon. The reason he wanted the 123's was because of the bailout hatch. That was a hole in the floor of the aircraft that would allow a crew member to lie down.

"He would have a starlight scope and look straight down for trucks. So, on some nights the 123 would be trolling up and down the trail looking for trucks. If they found any, they could light them up with flares. They would notify the air control for that night, it was usually a C-130 command plane, and the command plane would call in assets that were available."

"It could be Nimrods, or T-28's or it could be F-4's. If there were no FAC in the area the 123 would take on those duties. Some nights, though, they would fly in support of good guys. Some good guys would be under attack and the Candlesticks would fly to them and light up the night to keep the bad guys from launching sneak attacks. They took a lot of flak and anti-aircraft fire.

"Sometimes, when you lit up a convoy, you could see the North Vietnamese getting out of the trucks and running into the jungle. That is when the FAC or the Candlestick would call in the Nimrods or fighters to napalm the sides of the convoy about 50 yards into the jungle. That would box them in. At that point, the Nimrods or fighters would come in and destroy the convoy and the people operating it."

Jesse sat contemplating what the old man had just said. He knew it was true because he had done it himself. It was never written up that way in the reports. It was just noted that the fast movers had laid down ordnance. It was just how it was. It was just another night for the Laotian Highway Patrol.

"Boy, I sure am glad we did not have to do that every night," said Jesse. "Me too." said the old man, as Jesse started to clean up the coffee cups and Elder yawned.

"I start to get tired earlier and earlier. I don't know why; I get plenty of sleep." Jesse looked up from the sink and said, "It's just the weather. The colder it gets, the less I want to do." "I guess you're right. Why don't you bring Ryan and his boys next time? I'll tell them about the Son Tay raid," suggested Elder. "I might just do that," replied Jesse. "I never get tired of hearing about that." And with that the men shook hands and Jesse started to leave. "I will see you Tuesday. Are you coming to the house for Thanksgiving?" "Where else would I be?" said the old man, smiling. "Good, tell Sgt. Taylor he is invited too, OK?" Jesse said. "You got it," replied Elder. And with that Jesse headed home.

Martin

Photo by, USAF photo

A-26 Nimrod

Martin

#9

of the

Sagas of the Air Commandos

The Son Tay Raid

The orderly helped Elder into a good shirt. They
were through with the bathroom and the old man

was excited. It was Tuesday. On Tuesday Jesse, his only good friend, came to see him. Today was a special day. Jesse was bringing his son, Ryan and his grandsons with him. It was supposed to be a surprise but Sgt. Taylor down the hall had overheard them on the phone making lunch reservations for them. He was always glad to see the boys. He envied Jesse. Jesse had the family that the old man had never had. You make decisions in this life; you can have a successful career in combat arms or a family, but it is hard to have both. The old man knew Jesse had had his struggles, but he came out of it with a great family. And now that family was really all the old man had. He was excited today because the boys liked him to tell them stories about the war. He was always careful not to get too graphic or to put himself or Jesse in a bad light.

Of course, there had been bad times and close calls; it was a war. But these boys were too young to understand that, and they shouldn't have to. He heard them coming down the hall. Jesse, his son Ryan, and the two boys, James, the older one and his little brother, Ben. They were good boys and the old man loved having them visit.

Martin

There was a knock at the door and the old man heard a familiar greeting. "How's it going, Colonel?" asked Jesse. The old man turned toward the door and let go with a hearty "Never better." The boys ran in and gave the old man hugs and Jesse and Ryan came through the door smiling. After some small talk, the old man always had to know what was happening in school and with basketball practice. Elder brought out a sheaf of papers that his buddy CMSgt. Taylor had printed off the internet for him. Taylor had his own internet connection and the two of them did a lot of research in government archives.

The old man held up the papers and looked at the group and said, "Boy, do I have a story to tell you boys today." The boys, excited now, said in unison, "What is it?" The old man looked at them and said, "I am going to tell you the story of the Son Tay raid." Now, the boys, of course, had never heard of Son Tay or the raid. Ryan knew what it was, but knew very little about it. Jesse, of course, knew all about Son Tay. He wasn't on the raid, but the raid was used as a training tool for SOF. Jesse looked at the old man and grinned. He got up to make a pot of coffee. It would be straight today. They never juiced up the coffee when the boys were there. "Well," started the old man, "it all began like this.

"Back in 1968, USAF intelligence began to suspect that a compound in the Village of Son Tay was being used as a prisoner of war camp. They had aerial photos from SR-71 spy planes and Buffalo drones, plus intelligence that was gathered through other sources.

"They concluded in early May of 1970 that the camp contained 55 POWs and they determined that six of them were in dire need of medical help. They were recommending that the prisoners be rescued. Now," said the old man, "this was not a trivial recommendation.

"There were 12,000 North Vietnamese troops stationed within five minutes of Son Tay and there was an air base. Strike aircraft could be there in minutes. There were 200 or so guards for the camp living across the road. It boggles the mind just thinking about it. They took all of their intel and their recommendations to the Deputy Director of Plans and Policy and USAF Headquarters, Brigadier General James Allen. He studied the intel and the recommendations and when he was convinced of the fact that POW's were there, he took the information to Brigadier General Don Blackburn. Blackburn was Special Assistant for Counterinsurgency and special ops in the Pentagon. He reported directly to the Chairman of the Joint Chiefs of Staff.

"Blackburn had also commanded the Studies and Observation Group in Vietnam. He was a real go-getter and he loved special operations. He loved the idea of a raid to rescue prisoners so he took the information to the Chairman of the Joint Chiefs, General Earl Wheeler. The Chairman authorized a feasibility study. This phase of the operation was called Polar Circle. It was a fifteen-man study group to go over all of the information and make a determination as to whether to go on or abandon the idea.

"They convened this group in early June and studied everything. The group concluded that there were 61 POW's at Son Tay and they needed to be rescued." The old man's eyes were bright as he got into the story. "Don Blackburn immediately recommended that he should lead the mission, but the higher-ups nixed that idea. He then chose Brigadier General LeRoy Manor as the overall commander of the operation. He had a background in special operations and was an excellent planner.

"He got together a group of specialists to plan this thing. They had to be good. Son Tay was in a very heavily defended area. There were MiGs and surface to air missiles and more ground troops than you could shake a stick at. This new phase, the planning phase was called Ivory Coast." James, the older of Jesse's grandsons raised his hand.

The old man stopped and kindly asked him what he needed. "Well," said James. "with all of that enemy around and the other defenses, how could you even consider trying to get in there to get the prisoners and get out?" The old man smiled broadly. "That is a very good question, young man, and there is a very simple answer to it. It is a principle that we learned in special operations. It simply states that you can get away with anything once." James eyes were big and excited. The old man continued. "You see, if they don't know you are coming, you can appear out of nowhere, get the job done, and disappear before they know what is happening. It's like a magic trick."

James was satisfied with the answer and the old man continued. "The first thing the planning group decided was window of opportunity. Once all of the information was analyzed, including weather, it was decided that about the third week of October or November would be the best. While Brigadier Manor and his people were getting into the planning stage, command of the ground forces was given to Colonel "Bull" Simons. Now Simons was a legend in Special Forces and he readily accepted the challenge. He immediately sent out a call for volunteers for a secret mission. The men did not know what, where or when the mission would take place.

"He had over 500 volunteers. He interviewed all 500 and chose 100 to go into training for the mission. The CIA used its people to create a scale model of the camp and named it Barbara, I don't know why. Everything was compartmentalized. No one knew anything they did not need to know. Brigadier Manor chose Eglin AFB as the rehearsal site.

"The Special Forces troops and the Air Crews were assembled at Eglin and began to practice. A full-scale replica of the camp was constructed at Eglin. There have been stories that the camp was put up every morning and taken down every night. That is not true. It was made out of poles in the ground covered with canvas. It was unrecognizable even in Satellite Photos. Bull Simons and his Green Berets rehearsed the mission 170 times. They did it over and over again until Manor and Simons were satisfied that they were ready to go. All this time, the Air Force practiced the insertion and extraction of the men. The men practiced the actual assault on the POW camp. The Marines and the Navy knew nothing of the mission; the rest of the Air Force and the Army knew nothing of the mission.

"Only a small group of people knew what the mission was, even the people undertaking the mission did not know where they were going or why. Most thought it was a hostage rescue from terrorists somewhere in the world.

"All this time the planners were trying to cover all of the bases. They had intelligence that the prisoners may be shackled to their beds. Bolt cutters were issued to the assault team." Jesse got up to fill coffee cups and find out if anyone needed to go to the bathroom. Little Ben did, so his dad, Ryan, took him. The old man opened a drawer and pulled out an unopened package of chocolate chip cookies. "I know everyone here likes these. I had Taylor get them for me on one of his runs." Everyone agreed wholeheartedly and passed the cookies around. Ben and Ryan returned and got their cookies and the old man settled in to tell the story. "Now," said the old man, "Brigadier Manor was a great planner. He held meetings on the USS America with Vice Admiral Fred Bardshar. His part of the mission was one of creating confusion. He would send his naval aviators to fly circles over Phuc Yen Air Base. This is the base that housed the MiGs that flew night missions.

"There was a bombing ban at the time so they would not drop ordnance but would pin the MiGs on the ground, forcing North Vietnam to use missiles for defense instead of MiGs. People tend to downgrade this action by the Navy. What you have to remember is that those Navy boys were flying into enemy territory at night,with no ordnance, just to keep the MiGs on the ground. They were directly engaged with the enemy. Charlie could still shoot missiles at them, and did. The mission would not have succeeded without that diversionary action. Every single part of a Special Operation is important to every other part. Those Navy boys created such a ruckus that the Raiders were able to get in and get out.

"The Admiral had no idea what else would be going on. He did know that authorization was coming directly from the Joint Chiefs of Staff in the Pentagon. The Naval Aviation attack would also turn the North Vietnamese Radar to the East. The Raiders would be coming in from the West.

"Now this next part is kind of sad in a way. In September, Brigadier Manor went to see the Secretary of Defense, Melvin Laird. General Manor advised the Secretary that the team was ready to go during the October window of opportunity.

Martin

"Laird then met with the National Security Advisor, Henry Kissinger and he moved the launch to the November window. This was done due to the fact that President Nixon was not in Washington, so he could not be briefed on the raid in time for the October date." Ryan, Jesse's son, raised his hand. The old man paused the story and asked him what he needed. "Well," said Ryan. "It sounds like the Green Berets were practicing every day and night on the camp. What were the Air Commandos doing?" The old man started nodding his head and said. "That is a very good question, I tend to gloss over that part since we know what happened. Our Air Commandos flew over 1,000 hours of practice over Alabama, Georgia, and Florida. The reason this was necessary was because they were flying low level night formations with dissimilar aircraft. That means that we had a C-130 Combat Talon flying lead and then six big HH-3E Jolly Green Giant rescue helicopters. The second C-130 led the strike force of A-1E's. We had to have the C-130's to provide navigation for the Raiders and the strike force. Once on site, they would provide command and control and radio links to the Command Center. Practice ended during the second week of November and the entire group of operational personnel moved to Takhli Royal Thai Air Force Base.

Martin

"The Combat Talon C-130's left Eglin under the Call signs of Draw 43 and Thumb 66. They were pretending to be a part of an ongoing operation named Heavy Chain. They left Eglin on 10 November and flew to Norton AFB in California and then routed through Hickam AFB, Hawaii then to Kadena AB in Okinawa, arriving at Takhli on 14 November.

"The day after they left Eglin, the Army troops and equipment were transported by C-141's, one per day for four days. This was to make sure there was not an appearance of a major operation. The troops were not joined by their assault aircraft to keep the secrecy level high.

"The plan was for the first helicopter to go into the compound and literally crash land. It had the assault group. This group was made up of 14 Special Forces troops. Their code name was Blue boy. They would land and egress the aircraft and secure the inside of the compound. The second group would land outside of the compound, egress the aircraft, blow a hole in the compound wall and enter to assist Blue boy. Their code name was Greenleaf and there were 22 of them. The third group was to land outside of the compound and set up a defensive perimeter against the enemy trying to repel the raid.

Martin

"There were 20 of them and their code name was Red wine. Now, all of the troops and aircraft are in Thailand. The men spent the time getting their equipment ready and waiting for a Go. Now, nothing ever goes completely to plan, and this was no exception.

"The commanders were watching the weather. Typhoon Patsy hit the Philippines on November 18. The good news was that the weather guys said that a cold front would make good conditions for the raid on the 20th and bad after that. On the 20th the raiders would have clear sailing and the Navy flyers would have good clear flying. Remember, that Navy action was important. They flew a recon mission on the afternoon of the 20th. The decision had to be made. It was either go today, or wait at least five days. General Manor issued the order for the mission to Go.

"The group left Takhli around eleven at night. They flew to Udorn Air Base and met up with their helicopter transports. They had an uneventful flight to the target area. There was a Combat Talon C-130 code name Cherry 01 to lead the helicopters into North Vietnam to the target. It had to be something to see, a C-130 flying slow, leading a group of six of the Jolly Green Giant helicopters. It was a big V formation.

"There was a second C-130 Combat Talon, code name Cherry 02 to lead the A-1E strike mission. This left a little after the helicopters because the airspeed of the A-1's is faster. Blue boy was commanded by Captain Richard Meadows, Greenleaf was commanded by the mission Commander Bull Simons, and Red wine was commanded by Lt. Col. Elliot Sydnor. Those boys were ready and armed to the teeth. They had M-16's, CAR-15's, grenade launchers, hand grenades, and Claymore mines. They were issued axes, crowbars, and bolt cutters in case the prisoners were shackled. They also carried four M60 machine guns. Airplanes started to crank up and leave their bases at about 10:00 p.m. on November 20, 1970. Cherry 01 and Cherry 02 were leaving Udorn AB in Thailand. Two HC-130P aerial refuelers, code name Lime 01 and Lime 02, took off from Udorn.

"Everyone was flying in blackout conditions and ran into cloud cover and could not see to refuel. They went to 7,000 ft. AGL, to refuel." Young James raised his hand at this. Elder stopped and asked him what he needed. "What is AGL?" he asked. The old man smiled and kindly told the young man it stood for above ground level. "Thanks for stopping me James, I have to understand that everyone does not know these abbreviations." He then continued.

Martin

"Five A1-E Skyraiders took off from Nakhon Phanom in Northern Thailand. The helicopters met up with Lime 01 and Lime 02 and refueled. The refuelers then handed them off to Cherry 01 and Cherry 02.

"This was a rough trip. The flight path was a six-mile-wide corridor and consisted of 12 legs. Pilots of both formations had to be on their toes. They were flying at 1,000 feet above ground level in the valleys. The HH-3E helicopters had trouble climbing in formation and the C-130's had sluggish flight controls at the slow airspeeds and the A1-E's were struggling with heavy ordnance loads. While the Raiders were approaching the target area from the west, The Navy launched aircraft from two carriers, the USS Oriskany and the USS Ranger. It was the largest carrier night operation of the war.

"They launched 20 A-7 Corsairs and A-6 Intruders, flying in pairs and different altitudes and coming in to North Vietnam in three attacks. They were dropping flares to simulate an attack. They dropped chaff to simulate mining Haiphong Harbor and out over the South China Sea there were 24 other aircraft providing support. Needless to say, this operation caused the North Vietnamese to panic and use all of their Air Defense assets against the attack.

Martin

"This provided the perfect diversion for the Raiders. It was a little after two in the morning when they got there. Cherry 01 sent out the execution command of Alpha Alpha Alpha to all aircraft. Then Cherry 01 dropped flares and battle simulators over the compound. They then dropped napalm markers for the A-1's and left the area. They staged over Laos to be able to provide steering vectors for aircraft leaving the area. Apple 03, the gunship helicopter, arrived and strafed the guard towers with side firing mini guns.

"The Jolly Green Giant helicopter carrying Blue boy crash landed, as planned, inside the Son Tay compound. Capt. Meadows and Blue boy carried out their mission perfectly. The guards were taken out and the compound was secured. Meanwhile, Bull Simons and Greenleaf landed at the wrong spot." The old man held up his hand. "Now before you start in on Greenleaf, remember they were not flying the helicopter. The Air Commandos were. It wasn't incompetence, there was another compound that looked the same, and it was dark. So, Bull Simons ends up in another compound. They egressed from the helicopter and instead of blowing a hole in the wall to enter Son Tay, they found themselves in a compound that had been identified as the school. Unfortunately, it contained over 200 North Vietnamese soldiers.

"They had surprised the soldiers so Simons ordered the men to attack. Their records show they killed 100-200 soldiers before the rest ran away. They then reboarded their helicopter and flew to the right compound.

"In the meantime, Red wine, having seen Greenleaf land at the school and egress the aircraft, had arrived to secure the perimeter and put into effect the contingency plan. They filled the gap by blowing the wall and sending a team in to support Blue boy. Simons arrived at the compound a few minutes later. Capt. Meadows and Blue boy searched in vain for the POW's. After a few minutes it became clear that they were not there. Meadows' radio message clearly stated that the items they had come for were not there.

"The Green Berets cleared the extraction zone. They blew up an electric tower that blacked out the entire area, including Son Tay. The A-1's were ordered to attack the vehicle bridge over the Song Con river. They called for the helicopters to come for the extraction; they were hovering about a mile away. A truck convoy approached the area from the south but was stopped by two teams from Red wine with anti-tank missiles. The first team left the compound at 2:36 a.m. Everyone was gone in a few minutes. They had been on the ground for 27 minutes.

Martin

"There was a flurry of SAM's fired at the support aircraft. We had F-105's in the area. We called them Wild Weasels. They suppressed enemy radar that was used to guide the SAM's. One of the F-105's was damaged and the crew had to bail out over Laos. Alleycat, the Airborne Command and Control Center flying over Laos controlled the rescue. We covered those guys with aircraft, including a C-123 Candlestick flare ship. With all of that support, they were picked up at first light by SAR, Search and Rescue.

"They were all back in Thailand by 4:30 a.m. We had sent 56 Green Berets and 28 aircraft with 92 airmen to Son Tay. These aircraft had direct roles in the raid. All total there were 116 aircraft - 59 Navy and 57 Air Force.

"The only casualty of the raid was a flight engineer of the Blue boy helicopter. He had broken his ankle when the fire extinguisher broke loose during the crash landing." James raised his hand and the old man nodded to him. "Where were all of those other airplanes?"

Elder smiled and said, "where weren't they? Remember the assault team flew in with a C-130 combat talon leading six helicopters. There were backup C-130's, backup helicopters, and remember the Navy were flying on the east coast. And we had Air Commando A-1E's flying support out of Thailand. So, they were everywhere."

The young man nodded his head in understanding and then asked, "What happened to the guys that went on the raid?" "Well," said the old man, "they got medals and went back to their units as heroes." The young boy thought about this and then said. "How can they be heroes if no one was there? The old man sat and looked at the boy thoughtfully. "You have a good one there, Ryan, we are gonna make a pilot out of him yet." Everyone laughed and then the old man started talking. "Well, you know it's a shame, but there were people in the government that knew that camp was empty. Everything is so compartmentalized that one hand couldn't wash the other. This mission was so secret that people that knew about the camp knew nothing about the raid. But the raid is considered a success.

"It was criticized because they thought it would result in the prisoners being treated worse. That was not the case. If they had been treated worse, they would have died. What really happened after the raid was that prisoners were brought together; they were allowed to talk to each other and the food and conditions got better. That comes from the prisoners not the planners. This mission will go down in history as a well-planned, well executed rescue attempt. It was planned and executed on the wrong intelligence. I think that part has been worked out."

James was looking kind of pensive and he asked. "Would you have gone on that mission?" The old man smiled broadly and said "I sure would, I would have jumped at the chance." James turned around and said. "What about you, Grandpa?" "Yes," said Jesse, "I would have begged them to let me go."

The old man sipped his coffee and ate his cookies and looked over the group. James said that it all sounded too dangerous for him. The old man smiled and said "A friend of mine once told me that once you join the military, war fighting is your business. You fight to maintain the grand experiment of freedom. You fight so that boys like you and your brother can have the life you want. You can study what you want, live where you want, marry who you want, it all comes with being free.

"The U.S. is really the only truly free country in the world. Once you see other countries and see how other people live, you know that it is worth whatever it takes to keep America free." "Truer words were never spoken," said Jesse, "but, time is flying by and I need to get this group back to the house." James stood up and said, "but I want to hear another story." Jesse reached down and picked up the little one who had fallen asleep on the floor and told James, "maybe next time. I know the Colonel has some

good ones stashed away." The old man looked up with a
smile, "next time," he said, "I will tell you about how the Air
Commandos started and about General Heinie Aderholt, Air
Commando One."

#10

of the

Sagas of the Air Commandos

Brigadier General Harry C. "Heine" Aderholt

Air Commando One

Martin

The old man bent over his desk from his wheelchair and studied the papers stacked there in front of him. His friend, CMSgt. Taylor, had his own internet connection and knew how to use it. Taylor would find what the old man wanted and would print it out and bring it to him. Today's pile was a lot of biographical information about General Hienie Aderholt. He was affectionately known as Air Commando One, the Father of the Air Commandos. The old man was making sure he had covered all of the times that he wanted. His friend, Jesse, was bringing his son and his grandsons today to hear about Air Commando One. The old man was 94 years old and he knew he would not make it too much longer. When he passed away, he wanted Jesse to be able to tell these stories. There will always be room for a story about ordinary men doing extraordinary things. CMSgt. Taylor was coming today. The old man, Jesse, and Taylor had all known the then Colonel and later General Aderholt.

The old man would tell the boys today that Hienie Aderholt was a great man, a great pilot, and a great commander. If you met a man like Aderholt and stick with him, it will be a good ride. "How's it going, Colonel?" The old man was startled. He had not heard them approach.

Martin

He turned quickly and responded with his
trademark, "never better." There stood his friend Jesse and
his son Ryan. "Where are those boys of yours?" he asked
Ryan. "They are with their other grandparents today,"
Ryan told him, "and couldn't get out of it." They laughed at
that. Jesse was the old man's only true friend, and he was
already at the counter making a pot of coffee. "How are
you feeling?" asked Jesse. The counselor at the Veterans
Home had called him because the old man had fallen out of
his wheelchair. He had a couple of knocks and scrapes, but
nothing life threatening. The old man looked up and said.
"I guess they called you, huh?"

"Well," said Jesse, they just said you tried to jump
out of your wheelchair without a parachute." Jesse and
Ryan laughed at this joke, but the old man did not think it
was funny. "I'll be OK," he said. "I just wasn't paying
attention to what I was doing." Jesse was still smiling and
told the old man that he had better be careful. They were
going back and forth with this type of banter when Ryan
interrupted them and asked about General Aderholt. His
dad had told him what today's story was to be about.
"Yes," said the old man, as he gathered up some papers,
"Air Commando One. Well, you know we both started in the
same place.

Martin

"The Japanese had just attacked Pearl Harbor and we both signed up for the Army. We both applied to the Air Cadet program and were accepted. We both made it through the program and were commissioned as Second Lt. I took off to fly cargo planes, the C-47's, and Hienie went to Europe to fly bombers and eventually C-47's. You see, Hienie was not just a Bomber pilot, or a cargo pilot; later on he was a fighter pilot.

"Hienie Aderholt loved to fly. He flew big airplanes and, he could fly most of them by himself. That is something that I never did and did not want to do. But Hienie could fly darn near anything. He was never qualified in jets. That is because jets were never what he needed to accomplish the mission. The difference between people like me and General Aderholt is that he liked to command. He was a planner and an expediter. I just wanted to fly. I was flying C-47's in the Pacific when this English Commander named Ord Wingate came up with a plan to march his soldiers overland from Burma and attack the Japanese from the rear. As crazy as it sounded, it was approved. It was during the planning stages that they realized that the soldiers, called Chindets, would need to be re-supplied by air.

"Now me and my boys had been flying the hump to resupply ground troops, so this was right up our alley. So, we became the First Air Commando Squadron and Wingate and his boys set off into the Jungle.

"Me and my boys started flying supply missions. It was dangerous flying and we lost some birds doing that. Meanwhile, Capt. Aderholt was flying God knows what in Europe. Someone had to drop the resistance supplies and people behind enemy lines. It was at that time that the Air Commandos began. After the war, the Brass could get rid of Air Commando Squadrons, but they could not get rid of Air Commandos. Once Special Operations is in your blood, it never goes away. If I could, I would go fly a mission today." The old veterans all nodded their heads and said, 'me too.'

"Aderholt wanted to fly fighters and when the Korean war broke out, he saw his chance. He wanted to go to Korea and fly fighters against the enemy. The Air Force saw it differently. They needed experienced multi-engine pilots for cargo and they were not going to lose that experience, when they could train a new pilot to fly the jets. So Hienie goes off to Korea to fly C-47's. It was here that the rest of his career took shape. It was in Korea that Hienie would fly endless artillery re-supply missions.

"It was Hienie that would land under fire and taxi as close to the guns as he could get and then sit there while it was offloaded. There was no such thing as crew rest in that war zone. You flew as much as you could. Now, as with any unit, some of the pilots wanted to fly a regular schedule and some of them wanted to fly all of the time. Let's just say that if you wanted to fly you could, all you wanted.

"It was in that 1950-51 time period that Hienie was assigned to a small group of special aircraft. These aircraft and pilots were sent on very dangerous, life and death missions. It was here that he developed drop missions in the heat of combat. He would fly deep insertion missions to airdrop Korean Agents into North Korea. Agents from our country would recruit north Korean defectors to go back into the North and spy for us. They would then make their way back to our lines to be captured again and our agents would retrieve them.

"Hienie would fly them into North Korea at night and drop them by parachute. They had no jump experience, only some ground instruction. Now, you might ask, how did we get them to do this? It is very simple; they hated the Chinese and the north Koreans. Their families had been brutalized or killed by them. They wanted to strike back, and this was one way open to them.

"This was a very successful operation and we gathered a lot of important intel from them. One of the groups that Hienie and his pilots flew for was the CIA. They were the ones running the agents that Hienie and the boys were dropping at night. It got so that any difficult and dangerous mission they had would be assigned to Hienie Aderholt. They were impressed, and recruited him to come back to Washington to work at CIA headquarters. The CIA introduced paramilitary operations to Hienie Aderholt and his pilots. I was there at the time and that is where I got to know the now Major Aderholt.

"He, on the other hand, set up the Air Training School at the CIA training center they called The Farm. I will tell you a little secret. The pilots there thought this was the most exciting thing they had ever done, but, Hienie was bored.

"He wanted an exciting, special operations assignment. He looked around, but all the special operations wings in Korea were downgraded and eventually deactivated. Major Aderholt worked his way through several headquarters' assignments and finally, in 1957, he returned to the CIA. The Air Force was growing rapidly, but mainly in strategic air power.

"Nuclear bombers SAC was where it was at. The money and time went into SAC. Hienie was the Air Force guy at the CIA. The CIA would send him to straighten out problem areas. This suited Hienie just fine. He had just finished a tour with the CIA light aircraft operations. [Trest]

"Both the CIA and Hienie knew that these cold war brush wars, and wars of liberation were right up their alley. This is where his knowledge and expertise in Counterinsurgency came about. The CIA asked him if he could go to Kadena, Okinawa to straighten out a troubled operation there. He gladly accepted and was off to the Asian wars.

"Now this outfit in Kadena was flying covert support missions through Takhli, Thailand, to the partisans in Tibet. The Chinese had invaded and were taking over Tibet. The Dali Lama was in exile and the partisans were the only resistance. They were fighting an insurgency. Major Aderholt was with them in spirit. The new, at the time, C-130's filled the bill for a large airlifter that could drop and air land on short strips. Hienie trained the pilots, flew the missions, and got the entire operation running like a well-oiled machine. The CIA had operations there that supported covert activities in Laos and the entire area as well. Hienie became an integral part of their air operations.

"In 1961, newly elected Pres. John Kennedy had communist guerilla activities seemingly everywhere. He flinched on the Bay of Pigs. Hienie had helped the CIA train pilots for the invasion of Cuba using the Alabama National Guard. The initial invasion force was ready to go, and we had air power, A1-E's and A-26's staged in Central America. Everything was ready to go. Kennedy pulled crucial air power from the invasion and it failed. After the debacle, Kennedy knew he needed special operations forces and Hienie Aderholt and his band of special operations pilots became a hot commodity. Kennedy wanted Counter-insurgency capabilities and Hienie was made Lt. Col. It was a match made in heaven. Hienie was over in Kadena, making sure all missions were running smoothly and looking for new ones." The old man stopped talking and looked around the room. Everyone was listening attentively. He looked at Jesse and asked, "is that coffee done yet?" Everyone loosened up and got up to stretch their legs. CMSgt. Taylor, from down the hall had joined them.

The old man produced a pint of good whiskey, the coffee was poured and spiked, and they all settled back down to enjoy it. Ryan, Jesse's son, asked. "How did you all stay together?"

The old man looked up from his coffee and smiled, "Good question, young man. You see, we did and we didn't. Hienie would get an assignment, say, to Kadena. Well, it may take him six months to a year to get the rest of us transferred to his outfit. We tried to get there from our end and he would pull strings on his. Eventually, we ended up flying together. And I do mean flying together. Hienie may have been the commander of these outfits, but he never asked a man to fly a mission that he wouldn't fly. He would fly missions as an aircraft commander when there was a shortage or, sometimes, you would be checking out to go fly in the morning or at night and Hienie would show up and say, 'I am your copilot tonight'. Nobody minded that at all; he was a great man and a great pilot. These flights also gave you some time alone with the commander.

"You could tell him how you thought things were going and any improvement you would make. He didn't always take the advice, but he always listened. " CMSgt. Taylor, in the back of the room started talking. "I remember 1961, we still had a chance in '61, '62. Col. Aderholt was working with the CIA and setting up Lima sites in Laos and running a good little Counter-insurgency. I don't know how it got away from us.

"B52's, fighter jets, and aircraft carriers left no place for big war machines in a little Counter-insurgency." The old man was nodding his head in agreement. "Well," he said, "Hienie was always a little different than the Brass would have liked, but there was always somewhere for him to hide until he was needed. He was in Kadena running Counter- insurgency operations in three or four countries and being successful at it. He was reassigned to Eglin as Assistant Director of Operations of the Special Air Warfare Center.

"It was here that the battle would heat up between Lt. Col. Hienie Aderholt and the Command structure of the United States Air Force. Hienie thought that we should be helping people help themselves with supplies, equipment, and training. These things would keep them alive and keep them fighting for themselves. Hienie Aderholt never thought we should fight someone's battles for them; thus, the rift between Hienie and the Brass. Hienie was made a full Colonel in 1964 and was given command of the 1st. Air Commando Wing. From here he was sent to the Philippines and on to Vietnam. While working with MACV he created the Joint Personnel Recovery Center or JPRC. This group gathered and disseminated information on missing and captured personnel and tried to rescue others.

"There was one rescue attempt that failed because the Air Force did not provide timely airlift that was needed. You see, the JPRC would find information on a prisoner of war and plan an operation to go rescue him. The JPRC would plan everything and request whatever air assets they needed from the 7th Air Force. They would look at the request and then use their own timetable, not the one needed. Hienie roundly criticized the 7th Air Force, and their commander took umbrage. He and Hienie, I would say, bumped heads after that, but it was more like midair collisions. Hienie's group would request a certain number and type of aircraft for an operation and Headquarters 7th Air Force, would send whatever they thought he needed. The problem was, it did not work. If the Air Commandos requested A-1E's for air support, it was because that was the best option to accomplish the mission. They would request them and then Headquarters would send F-100 jets that could not get under the cover and could not deliver their ordnance. In other words, they were useless.

"The Brass would have sent Hienie to Alaska if they could. But, instead, Hienie was sent to NKP Thailand. He was given command of the 56th Air Commando Wing. There he was in his glory.

Martin

"He was also under the 8th Air Force, not the 7th that gave him all of the trouble. He had a great civic action program; he was supporting Vang Pao over in Laos. But what really chapped the 7th Air Force commander was the night interdiction missions over the Ho Chi Minh trail. They were flying A-26's, A-1E's, FAC's and C-123's and were killing trucks at a rate you could not keep track of. On the other hand, fighter aircraft could do nothing at night and were too fast to see or hit anything in the jungle during the day. The Seventh wanted their higher and faster air force to get the credit, but Col. Hienie Aderholt stood in their way. If Hienie Aderholt had been in charge of Vietnam, we would have never had the big Army, big Air Force, or big Navy. We would have had training and support missions while the Vietnamese fought their own war. If we had done that, we would have saved nearly 50,000 American lives. Hienie Aderholt knew the difference between a little jungle war and WWII. The Brass did not. They wanted a big war and they wanted to make more general officers.

"They had their big war and they lost. They made a lot of generals but they were not efficient. So, what was gained? Colonel Aderholt made Special Operations a household word.

"He utilized what the Air Force would call unconventional aircraft: low flying FAC's, propeller driven fighters and bombers. This was TAC Air with planes from the smallest to the largest, aircraft gunships that virtually changed the game. Hienie was able to cultivate relationships with other services' special ops forces and put together teams that accomplished the most difficult missions.

"One of the things that drew attention to Hienie was his passion for developing methods of inserting agents or units behind enemy lines and being able to exfiltrate them when their mission was finished. Rescuing downed airmen was another of his passions, and working with the CIA, who had the same interest as the Air Force. Nobody knew that the CIA was not only running rescue operations for their own people, but were also running them for us over in Cambodia and Laos. It was Hienie who found the Helioplane. The Helioplane was a Short Takeoff and Landing, or STOL, aircraft. It could take off and land in a parking lot. Aderholt was showing the aircraft to one of the general staff and he pulled up to the runway and stopped in the taxiway to get takeoff clearance. When he was cleared, he stood on the brakes, gave it full throttle and took off across the width of the runway.

"The staff officer was shook up but duly impressed, and the Air Force ordered the Helioplanes that Hienie wanted. Testing that aircraft and getting it bought made Aderholt a star at the CIA. Downed crew recovery was very important to Hienie. He frowned upon missions that had no rescue capabilities. That's why when we first started operations in Thailand, in Laos, and in Cambodia the CIA ran rescue operations for us.

"Even today, the combat Talon C-130's have the Fulton recovery system installed." Ryan raised his hand and the old man stopped talking and nodded to him. "You have a question, young man?" asked the old man kindly. Ryan had a quizzical look on his face and asked, "what exactly is a Fulton recovery system?" The old man smiled as did the rest of the fellows and the old man rolled over to the wall that had most of his pictures on it and reached out and took one down. Elder rolled back over to Ryan and handed him the photo. "You see that framework on the nose of the aircraft?" "Yes," said Ryan. "Well," said the old man, "when a pilot went down, SAR, or Search and Rescue, went into action. Sometimes they would send A-1E's and Jolly Greens to pick them up. But sometimes that wasn't possible. The crewman could be down in the middle of a heavy enemy concentration.

"So, what they would do is get a fix on the crewman's location and they would fly a C-130 or 123 or even a Helioplane in at night at low level. They would drop him a Fulton package." "What's that?" asked Ryan. "Hold on," said the old man, holding up his hand, "I am getting to that." He then continued. "The Fulton package contained a rubberized coverall suit with a very long line attached to it. The other end of the line was attached to a large weather balloon. All special operations crew members are checked out on how to put on the suit and fill the balloon with the helium canister that comes with it. So, the downed airman would put on the suit and be ready to inflate the balloon and would send out a pre-arranged radio signal. That would alert the Air Commandos that were operating the Combat Talon to go snatch this boy back to the land of the living from the jaws of death. Now during this whole operation, a Combat Talon would be staged as close as they could safely get. When the signal was given that the downed airman was ready to go, the Talon would make its run to save the airman. The airman on the ground would now be in radio contact with the Talon. On the far end of the approach the pilot of the Talon would instruct the airman to inflate and launch the balloon.

"Once the balloon was inflated, the airman just had to let it go. It rose to the end of the line. Now the Talon pilot had to find it. He had to get a visual on the balloon as soon as he could because you really only had one shot at this. If he couldn't get a visual and had to go around, it is possible that the enemy could find our airman and it would be game over. And they might shoot down the Talon. But normally the Talon pilot gets a visual on the balloon and he lines up the aircraft. That framework on the nose of the airplane now opens up. It is now a big V and it is what is going to catch the line on the balloon. This is a very difficult task and it is a tribute to the pilots that do it. The pilot lines the plane up and runs right into the line and the V mechanism grabs the line and cuts off the balloon. Now when this happens the airman on the ground is sitting in the position that he has been trained in and is awaiting lift off. Because of the length of the line and the stretch of the suit he does not go from 0 to about 180 instantly. He is pulled up and away and gains speed quickly but safely. In a moment he is up in the air, being towed by a C-130. The mechanism on the aircraft transfers the line to the ramp in the back where the loadmasters and other crew attach a winch and reel our boy into the aircraft. To my knowledge, The Air Commandos are the only group that can do this."

Ryan is sitting in his chair with a look of shock on his face. "You mean, you pick him up off of the ground with a flying airplane?" The old man smiled and nodded his head. "That's right. I volunteered almost as many times as your dad did to do a test of the system and be picked up. It never happened for either of us. What a shame." CMSgt. Taylor, Jesse , Ryan and the old man passed the picture around. The old man broke the silence with, "Hienie Aderholt knew Bob Fulton. It was with support of Col. Aderholt and the Air Commandos that he was able to perfect that little engineering marvel.

"It has saved lives. How many lives, we will never know, but I know for a fact that it has been successfully used for the purpose it was designed. Our Air Commandos became the most capable Air Special Ops group in the world. Col. Aderholt brought it from a random thought to full functionality. Even as the Brass kicked and screamed about every airplane and every crew member, Hienie made it happen. He is directly or indirectly responsible for the majority of our rescue operations. Hienie would always go after a downed airman. When he first got to Thailand, he put a hoist on the side doors of all of his UH-1 Huey helicopters. He would go and rescue any of his pilots that were shot down.

"The Brass made him take them off. One of his guys got shot down over Laos and Hienie made the crew chief put one back on to go get the guy. The crew chief knew nothing about these hoists, but he put it on the best he could. When Hienie got there, he lowered the hoist and got the pilot on the penetrator. The cable broke halfway up because of no maintenance. The pilot died. Later a General was talking to Hienie about it and Hienie looked him in the eye and said, "I killed that man, because I listened to you. "(Trest) That was the kind of man Col. Hienie Aderholt was. The best Commander any of us ever had."

Photos by, USAF photo

Everyone commented about the legacy of Gen. Hienie
Aderholt. As they were talking CMSgt. Taylor noticed the
old man was nodding out. It was amazing how well a 94-
year-old man could tell the stories that he did. His mind
was as sharp as a tack, but his body was letting him down.
They rolled the wheelchair over to his bedside so an orderly
could get him into his bed. Taylor picked up a book named
Air Commando One by Warren A. Trest and showed it to
Jesse. We have all heard these stories about Gen. Aderholt,
but this book has it all. Jesse just smiled. "I gave that to
him for Christmas." They smiled at each other and then
cleaned up the coffee cups, hid the whiskey and said their
goodbyes. Jesse and his son Ryan went to their car and
started home. CMSgt. Taylor went back to his room.

Martin

On the way home, Ryan asked his father, "What's going to happen when Elder is gone?" Jesse looked pensive and told him that that time was very close at hand. "It will be me and CMSgt. Taylor to keep and tell the stories of the Air Commandos." Ryan looked at his father and asked him, "are you disappointed that I did not join the Air Force?" Jesse looked over and smiled. "No, not at all; a man, or a woman, has to choose their own path in life. You are an educator, a great musician, a great salesman, a great father and husband, and a wonderful son. I am very proud of you and your accomplishments. Just because they are different than mine does not make them less important." They were almost home when the phone rang. Jesse answered it because it was the nursing home where the old man lived. It was the call he had been expecting and dreading for a while now. Elder had passed away sitting in his wheelchair, where they had left him. Jesse was the guardian of the old man.

He turned the car around and headed back to the nursing home. He told his son Ryan. "Use my phone, call CMSgt. Taylor. Tell him to make sure nothing is taken out of that room before we get there. There are some items and paperwork that I need to get." Jesse arrived at the nursing home and the ambulance was there.

Martin

They had tried to resuscitate the old man but to no avail. He was lying on his bed in a body bag. Jesse went up to the bag and opened it. He made sure the old man had his Air Commando challenge coin in his hand and was wearing his Air Force ring. Jesse pulled out a signed power of attorney, which the nursing home already had on file. He instructed the funeral home personnel to make sure that that ring and that coin stayed with the Colonel at all times. After the cremation, what was left of the Coin and the ring was to be placed in the Urn containing the ashes. After finding out a time schedule for the cremation, Jesse called the Biloxi National Cemetery and arranged for the funeral and interment. He called The Air Commando Association to arrange for a color guard and to let the membership know that one of their beloved air warriors had flown his last mission.

When he was finished, he and Ryan got back into the car for the ride home. "I am sorry, Dad," said Ryan with sadness in his voice. Jesse looked over at him and told him, "It is alright, that time comes to all of us. The old man was right this morning when he woke up and said, 'It is a fine day to die'. Did you call your mother to let her know why we are late?" Ryan looked at his phone and said, "yeah, I tried to call and got voicemail, so I sent her a text."

Martin

"She was in the yard working and did not get the
call but she texted back how sorry she is and for us to take
our time." The two men were silent for the rest of the trip
home. Jesse was the old man now. He would go to see
CMSgt. Taylor and tell the stories of the Air Commandos to
men who were there, their children and their children's
children. The legacy had to live on.

Jesse was thinking to himself; a lot of things had
been accomplished by the Air Commandos since he was in.
Maybe it was time for a trip over to Hurlburt Field to talk to
some present-day Commandos. As he pulled into his
driveway, Jesse knew what he had to do.

As it was in WWII, Korea. And Vietnam

It is tonight

Anytime, Anyplace

Glossary

ARVN	Army of the Republic of Vietnam
NVA	North Vietnamese Army
PAVN	People's Army of Vietnam
Tweet	A37 Close air support fighter
CIDG	Civilian Irregular Defense Forces
Dust Off	UH-1 huey medivac helicopter
SNAFU	Situation Normal, All Fowled Up
LZ	Landing Zone
DZ	Drop Zone
AC	Aircraft Commander, Attack Cargo
Penetrator	Device lowered to pick up downed airmen
Feet wet	Flying overwater
AFSC	Air Force Systems Command
PJ	Jump Qualified Para rescue operator

Made in the USA
Middletown, DE
26 August 2022